Vancouver Island Shores

Seashore exploring for the novice

I. The eastern shoreline from Victoria to Campbell River (including the Gulf Islands)

written and illustrated by

Lynda A. Colbeck

For Bill and Greg

Published by
Protected Shores of Vancouver Island
#266, 9-B 1150 N. Terminal Avenue
Nanaimo, British Columbia V9S 5T8

Printed and bound in Canada by Transcontinental Printing, Inc.

CANADIAN CATALOGUING IN PUBLICATION DATA

Colbeck, Lynda A., 1953-
   Vancouver Island Shores: seashore exploring for the novice

   Includes bibliographical references and index.
   Contents: V. I.The eastern shoreline from Victoria to Campbell River (including the Gulf Islands)
   ISBN 0-9682002-0-6

   1. Seashore biology - British Columbia - Vancouver Island.
   I. Title.
QH95.7.C65 1998   578.76'09711'2   C97-910254-5

CONTENTS

Acknowledgements

This book would not have been possible without the help of **Dr. Timothy Goater**, instructor of invertebrate zoology, evolution and parasitology at Malaspina University-College in Nanaimo, BC. Dr. Goater's extensive knowledge and enthusiastic support of this project was invaluable.

Special thanks to **Linda Leger,** librarian at Malaspina University-College in Duncan and Nanaimo, BC, who contributed her keen copyediting skills and offered general editorial advice.

A very special thank you to my step-father and mother **Beatty and Ruby Mellow** for their contribution to this book.

Thanks also for the valuable scientific advice received from:
   Dr. Philip Lambert, Curator of Marine Invertebrate Zoology, Royal British Columbia Museum, Victoria, BC,
   Dr. Bill Austin, The Marine Ecology Station, Cowichan Bay, BC, and,
   Susan Yates, reference librarian at the Vancouver Island Regional Library System in Nanaimo, BC.

The **cover photograph** of the author's son, Greg Weller, was taken at a gravel and cobblestone beach at Eagle Point in the north end of Nanaimo, BC, in the spring of 1997.

INTRODUCTION

It was pink, had five rigid arms and a spattering of white beading over its entire surface. The lone sea star, almost hidden from view, huddled beneath the shaded ledge of a massive beach boulder. The blustery spring breeze off of the Strait of Georgia fluttered the pages of my open field guide.

Comparing my specimen to the photographs, I thought that I had found a Purple Sea Star, *Pisaster ochraceus*. But this particular animal was salmon pink rather than purple as shown in the photo and I wondered if it could be some other species.

**Purple
Sea Star**

Seashore exploring for the beginner

My initial trips to the beach were enormously frustrating.

First, I was overwhelmed by the large number of species, both common and rare, included in most seashore field guides.

Second, for species identification, I relied on colour photographs which sometimes proved misleading. Many species of animals have highly variable colouration. I needed to learn how to distinguish plants and animals from their shape and size as well as their colour.

Third, Pacific Northwest guides cover a large geographic area extending from Northern California to Northern British Columbia. Were the plants and animals found on the outer Oregon coast the same as those found on the quieter, more protected eastern shores of Vancouver Island?

Fourth, field guides emphasize species identification. I wanted not only to identify a creature but more importantly, learn about how it lived. What does it eat? How does it reproduce? How long does it live?

Common intertidal plants and animals

This book was written to help the novice seashore explorer learn about the most common and conspicuous animals and plants found along the shores of Vancouver Island.

Vancouver Island

Vancouver Island Shores Volume I discusses the eastern shoreline from Victoria north to Campbell River

Campbell River

Comox

Courtenay

Strait of Georgia

British Columbia

Nanaimo

Washington State

Duncan

Victoria

Intertidal plants and animals to look for

Vancouver Island Shores is organized into chapters that each describe a particular type of shoreline or beach. Within each chapter, a list of "Plants and Animals To Look For" is provided, followed by their natural history. Descriptions and illustrations of local species follow.

The "Plants and Animals To Look For" list is provided as an introductory guideline for novice seashore explorers and does not include all of the plants and animals that will or can be found. As well, although most marine animals and plants have preferences as to the kinds of shorelines they live on, many can be found on a variety of beach types.

Species identification

For this reason, each species description details the kinds of shorelines or substrates on which a plant or animal will be found. For species identification, check all chapters of the book, not just those of a particular beach type.

To keep a record of your seashore explorations, complete the species checklist of animals and plants and "Seashore Exploring Log" included at the end of each chapter. Observing tips and strategies will enrich your seashore experience.

Introduction to the diversity of intertidal life

Vancouver Island Shores describes in very general terms the natural history of many groups of plants and animals. The terms "most species" or "many species" are often used since many exceptions to generalizations exist. The seashore explorer should consider this guide as an introduction to the fascinating plants and animals found between the tides.

Volume I: from Victoria to Campbell River

Volume I discusses the Strait of Georgia shoreline from Cordova Bay north of Victoria to Elma Bay, south of Campbell River. It includes the Gulf Islands.

Seashore etiquette

Everyone interested in nature is well aware of the concern about inadvertently destroying the very things we are trying to discover and understand.

Did you know that..

low tide is the best time to go to the beach to find as many diverse animals and plants as possible?

Most provincial parks have a "look but don't touch" policy. Park officials are concerned that the stress of human intervention may adversely affect the animals. Common sense etiquette and respect for the shoreline and its inhabitants should be observed.

Tips for novice seashore explorers

- ✪ Think small. The stated size of marine animals in most guides, including this one, is the maximum adult size. Chances are you won't always find a fully mature animal.
- ✪ Look closely and be patient.
- ✪ Walk carefully. Try not to crush living things underfoot.
- ✪ Pick up animals gently and put them back in the position and in the place where you found them. If they are attached tightly to a hard surface, do not pull or force them off.
- ✪ Fill in any holes you have dug.
- ✪ Turn rocks over cautiously and place them back gently in their original positions.
- ✪ Do not collect live creatures.
- ✪ Be exceedingly selective about collecting empty shells and dead animals. They provide homes and food for other intertidal animals.
- ✪ Keep beaches clean. Pick up all bottles and cans, even if they are not yours.
- ✪ Adults and children must have a valid license to harvest seafood. Be aware that some beaches may be closed to shellfish harvesting due to paralytic shellfish poisoning.
- ✪ Be aware that many beaches are sites of shellfish aquaculture farms. Do not walk in these areas, particularly during low tide.

Common sense safety

✪ Know whether the tide is coming in or going out. Schedule trips to the beach a few hours before the time of lowest tide and start exploring in the low intertidal region and proceed toward the high intertidal region.

✪ Don't climb steep rocky cliffs.

✪ Avoid playing on floating drift logs and stumps.

✪ Never swim out to exposed sand bars where you could be stranded by tidal waters.

✪ Be very cautious near shores with swift off-shore tidal currents.

✪ Seaweed is slippery and some algae grow so thick on rocks that it is impossible to see deep crevices or holes.

Suggested equipment to take

✪ This book, ruler, and pencils.

✪ Magnifying glass to get a close-up look at small creatures.

✪ Camera with macro lens for close-up photographs.

✪ Forked trowel and bucket.

✪ Footwear that you don't mind getting wet.

✪ Drinking water.

✪ Backpack to carry extra clothes, hat, sunscreen, and small towel.

✪ Plastic bag to carry out refuse.

✪ Bandaids and first aid ointment for minor cuts and scrapes.

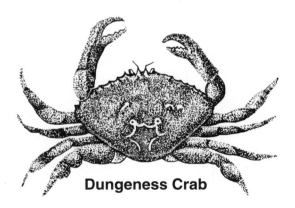

Dungeness Crab

Members of the Phylum Echinodermata

Sea Cucumber

Sand Dollar

Sea Star

Sea Urchin

Scientific names of animals and plants

It is often the case that books written for the layperson list animal and plant species by their common names. In *Vancouver Island Shores*, each species is listed by its scientific name with a guide to its pronunciation in square brackets. Its common name follows.

Common names are inconsistent

The reason to emphasize the use of scientific names is a pragmatic one. Common names are notoriously inconsistent. Many species in this book have two or three common names. Conversely, one common name can apply to two or three different species.

For the seashore explorer interested in learning more about a particular species or comparing photographs or drawings in various published field guides, the most consistent reference is the scientific name.

Scientific two-part name

Usually Latin, but sometimes Greek, the first name, the so-called genus, is always capitalized; the second, the species, is not. Both genus and species names always appear in italics or are underlined.

A species name can describe a unique physical feature, such as the Excentric Sand Dollar, *Dendraster excentricus.* The five-petal pattern on the sand dollar is slightly off-centre or in Latin, excentricus. A species name can describe the place where the species was first found or where it is only found. The marine Feather Duster Worm, *Eudistylia vancouverensis,* describes Vancouver as the place where it was first identified. The species name can also be named after the person who first discovered the species or in honour of a person. The Heart Cockle, *Clinocardium nuttallii,* was named in honour of the English naturalist and botanist, Thomas Nuttall.

References to particular species that are unknown or possibly one of a variety of species are presented as *Macoma sp.* The plural, *spp.* means more than one species of the genus are being referred to, as in *Macoma spp.*

Previously used scientific names

Even scientific names are apt to change as biologists learn more about these creatures. Scientific names that appear in parentheses in this book are previously used scientific names which the seashore explorer may find in some older field guides.

Taxonomy

Animals and plants are divided into a biological classification scheme that is based on an organism's anatomy, as well as its biochemistry, embryology, molecular biology, behaviour, ecology and evolutionary history. The study of the classification of animals and plants into their presumed natural relationships is called taxonomy.

Phylum	Animals and Plants
Annelida	segmented worms
Arthropoda	barnacles, crabs, hermit crabs, pea crabs, shrimps, isopods, amphipods
Cnidaria	jellyfishes, hydroids, sea anemones
Ctenophora	comb jellies
Echinodermata	sea stars, brittle sea stars, sand dollars, sea urchins, sea cucumbers
Mollusca	clams, oysters, snails, whelks, nudibranchs, limpets, mussels, chitons
Nemertea	ribbon worms
Porifera	sponges
Urochordata	sea squirts
Chlorophyta	green seaweeds
Phaetophyta	brown seaweeds
Rhodophyta	red seaweeds

Marine Animals and Plants Grouped According to Phyla

Phyla of animals and plants

Taxonomists group biologically similar plants and animals into phyla and many seashore field guides are organized according to this systematic arrangement. For example, the members of the phylum Echinodermata [ee-KINE-oh-der-MAT-ah] are the sea star, the sand dollar, the sea urchin and the sea cucumber.

The chart above groups the animals and plants discussed in *Vancouver Island Shores* into their scientific phyla.

BETWEEN THE TIDES

The Island, the Strait of Georgia, the Intertidal Animals and Seaweed

The Island

Lying between latitudes 48° and 51° N, Vancouver Island is primarily mountainous rainforest. From the southeast to the northwest tip of the Island, it measures about 520 kilometres (280 miles) in length.

The east coast, from north of Victoria at Cordova Bay to Elma Bay south of Campbell River, stretches 250 kilometres (150 miles) by the Trans Canada and Island Highways. The shore along the Strait of Georgia is described geologically as a protected coastline, since it is remote from the open Pacific Ocean and is not subjected to the large waves and storms that often batter the west coast of the Island. The Gulf Islands, of which there are over 200, are nestled along the southeast coast of the Island.

Common Shore Types

The shoreline between Victoria and Campbell River, including most of the Gulf Islands, is part of the geological or physiographic region known as the Nanaimo Lowlands.

Rocky shorelines

Rocky shorelines are composed largely of sandstone, shale or conglomerate rocks. The erosive effects of winter storm waves and water runoff have cut deep crevices and caverns into these soft, sedimentary rocks.

Gravel and cobblestone beaches

Cobblestone and gravel beaches are often found at the base of a forested sea cliff in the lee of rocky headlands. At high tide, the beach consists of a narrow cobblestone and boulder foreshore. At low tide, pockets of mud and sand can be found intermingled with gravel and large boulders.

Mud flats

Mud flats are typically found at the head of long bays or harbours and at the mouths of major rivers and creeks. Fresh water deposits silt and mud from river beds into the strait where they are often mixed with sand. These finer sediments are not pulled out into deeper waters due to the gentle waves and currents found in protected bays and harbours.

Sandy beaches

Long sandy beaches are found on the east side of Saanich Peninsula and from Parksville to north of Comox. These spectacular beaches were created by glaciers from the last ice age of just over 15,000 years ago.

Smaller or pocket sandy beaches, common at the heads of protected inlets and bays, are created by the deposit of fine sediment by gently lapping waves.

The Intertidal Region

The intertidal region is where water and land meet. It is a small strip of coastline, continuously covered and uncovered by the daily action of the tides.

Between the low tide and hide tide mark

The intertidal region begins at the highest point on land where sea water touches or splashes and ends at the place where the sea water recedes at the lowest tide.

How wide is it?

The width of the inter-tidal region broadens or narrows depending upon the seashore's bottom or sub-strate.

A long sandy beach, like Parksville Beach, has a very gentle slope out into the Strait of Georgia. The overall distance between the high water and low water mark can measure as much as 300 metres (975 feet).

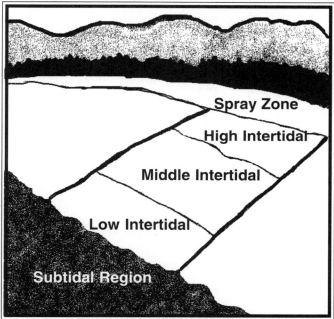

The Intertidal Region At Low Tide

Conversely, the distance between the high and low tide marks on a steep rock face, like those off Newcastle Island near Nanaimo, can be measured at less than 10 metres (32.5 feet) apart. The intertidal region accordingly is as narrow or as broad as the sub-strate dictates.

Mixed substrate within intertidal region

Many beaches along the east coast of Vancouver Island are composed of a variety of substrates. Very typical in bays and inlets are rocky, sandstone shores with small pockets of gravel and sand beaches. At the foreshore, the beach can be predominately gravel and becomes sandier and muddier toward the low water mark.

The Strait of Georgia

The Strait of Georgia has been compared to an enclosed lake, and when seen on a map, it is easy to appreciate why. Access to the open Pacific Ocean is almost cut off by islands and very narrow passages.

Almost an enclosed estuary

To the north, the narrow entrance at Johnstone Strait impedes the flow of tidal waters, while to the south, the long arduous journey through the Strait of Juan de Fuca and up through the Gulf Islands can delay tidal water flow for up to six hours. Of course, these land mass barriers give the Strait its unique tidal currents and eddies and enhance the mixing of salt ocean waters with fresh water runoff.

Plenty of fresh water runoff

Although almost eighty per cent of the fresh water entering the Strait originates from the Fraser River on the mainland, five fresh water estuaries (Cowichan River Estuary, Nanaimo River Estuary, Comox River Estuary, Campbell River Estuary, and Englishman River Estuary) on the east coast of Vancouver Island assist in the process.

Fresh water runoff contains chemical and mineral elements of great importance to the nutritional needs of all marine plants and animals.

Johnstone Strait

Campbell River

Comox River

Strait of Georgia

Englishman River

Nanaimo River

Cowichan River

Fresh Water Estuaries and Surrounding Straits

Strait of Juan de Fuca

Fresh and salt water are blended

Fresh water tends to lie on the surface of the denser or heavier salt water, but when ebbing tidal waters carry the fresh surface waters out to sea, the tidal action in the San Juan Strait mixes the two. When the tide returns, the sea water is a blend of the nutritionally rich fresh and salt water.

Less salty than the open ocean

With the influx of large quantities of fresh water, the Strait is considerably less salty than the open ocean waters. The average water salinity in the open Pacific is about 3.5 per cent. The Strait of Georgia's salinity averages anywhere from 2.9 to 3.1 per cent.

Brackish water

Brackish water occurs around the mouths of rivers or where fresh water from rain or snow or small underground streams seeps into the Strait. Brackish water is usually considered to be less than 1.7 per cent salt.

The importance of upwellings

During the summer months, the lighter brackish water is blown away from the shoreline by winds and carried out into deeper waters of the Strait with the tidal currents. Deeper saltier waters, full of organic and inorganic matter, surge up to the surface to replace the fresh water. This process, called upwelling, provides a continuous supply of food and oxygen for marine animals and plants living in the Strait.

Origins of the Strait

The Strait of Georgia originated not as a river but from the continuous folding of the earth's crust. It is part of the Georgia-Hecate Depression which runs almost 4,000 kilometres (2,400 miles) from Alaska to the Gulf of California.

On average, the Strait is 33 kilometres (20 miles) wide, 155 metres (504 feet) deep and about 220 kilometres (132 miles) long.

Did you know that... over long, shallow, sandy beaches along the Strait of Georgia, the water temperature can reach up to 23° Celsius (73° Fahrenheit)? On average, the surface water temperature in the winter months is 6° Celsius (43° Fahrenheit) and in the summer months, 18° Celsius (64° Fahrenheit.)

The Tides

The ocean's tides are a result of the complex orbits of the Earth, Moon and Sun around each other. Many physical forces create the tides.

Centrifugal and gravitational forces

Gravitational forces between the Earth and Moon keep each attracted to the other. As the two objects orbit around each other, centrifugal force on the Earth's surface causes the oceans to bulge on the side of the Earth closest to the Moon and on the directly opposite side of the Earth. This bulging creates high tides. Correspondingly, the waters in between are at low tide.

As the Earth revolves on its axis, the tides rise and fall over every part of the planet. Since the Earth spins once every 24 hours, there are two daily high tides and two daily low tides. At full and new moon, when the Moon and Sun are aligned, the combined or increased gravitational effect produces tides that are higher than normal, called spring tides. Conversely, when the Moon is near its first and third quarters, the gravitational effect causes the tides to rise lower than normal. These are called neap tides.

All tides are local

All tides are local. Out on the Pacific Ocean, the effect of the tides alters the surface waters on average only about 60 centimetres (2 feet). Many factors can effect the height and time of the daily tides. Surface winds over the water can delay or hasten the tide depending on their speed and direction. A changing atmospheric or barometric pressure can literally push down on the water creating less than anticipated high or low waters.

Along the east coast of Vancouver Island, the most significant factor affecting the tides is the impact of land on the flow of water. Tidal waters enter the Strait of Georgia from the south through the Strait of Juan de Fuca and from the north through Johnstone Strait.

Unequal height of the tides

The narrow passages at each entrance and exit slow the rate of tidal waters so profoundly that time of high tide is progressively later as one travels north from Victoria toward Campbell River. When the tidal waters have reached their maximum height in the strait, the water immediately begins to drain back out toward the ocean. As a result, the east coast of Vancouver Island experiences one very high tide followed by a very low tide, then a high tide followed by a very slightly "lower than high" low tide. These two high tides of unequal height and two low tides of unequal height are called mixed-semi-diurnal tides.

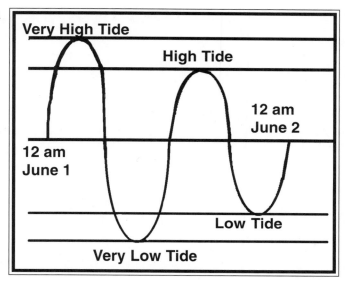

How to read a tide table

A weekly or monthly table is usually listed in local newspapers or is available free in booklet form in the *Annual Tide and Bite Guide For Local Waters*. Each day of the year is listed with the corresponding times for the lowest and highest height of tidal waters. Levels are listed in feet rather than metres. The height of the tide (HGT/FT) is the vertical distance between the water surface and marine navigational chart datum. For example, if the daily tide table indicates low tide will be one foot, to determine the actual depth of water, that number must be added to the depth shown on the navigational chart.

When to go to the beach

When low tidal datum is a small value (less than 2, for example), the lowest regions of the intertidal zone will be exposed to the air and encounters with plants and animals are maximized.

Tidal data stations

For shorelines north of Victoria, including the Saanich Inlet to Dodds Narrows, data are recorded from the Fulford Harbour Station on Saltspring Island. For shorelines from Dodds Narrows north to Campbell River, data from Point Atkinson, north of Vancouver, are used.

Did you know that...
the lowest low tides of the year during daylight hours along the east coast of Vancouver Island occur in late June and early July? Check your tide table for specific dates.

The Intertidal Animals

A harsh environment

More varieties and numbers of invertebrate animals live between the tides than in almost any other habitat on the planet. Living conditions are harsh. During low tide, organisms that are accustomed to being submerged in salt water must spend many hours of every day exposed to the open air. Those exposed to the air must endure the extremes of the seasons, from the drenching of rainfall and freezing temperatures in the winter to the blistering heat of the summer sun.

Animals need to retain moisture during low tide

To prevent or reduce the effects of water loss when exposed to the air during low tide, most mobile animals seek shelter and shade. Many retreat into tidepools, slip under rocks, or move down the shore towards low tide waters.

Sessile or attached animals close up their watertight shells or tightly tuck in their tentacles to reduce the effect of desiccation.

Animals live in bands or zones on the beach

Intertidal invertebrate animals are not found scattered randomly up and down the breadth of the intertidal region. Most have adapted to survive in a distinct zone of the intertidal region.

The intertidal zones vary from beach to beach, according to the extent of the rise and fall of the tidal water, the kind of sediment found along the shoreline, the amount of sunlight received, and a variety of other environmental factors. These zones are rather arbitrarily defined and the seashore explorers should note that many animals move about and overlap within them. However, they are helpful guides for the novice to locating intertidal animals and plants.

Speckled Limpet

The Intertidal Zones

Spray zone

The spray zone is a very small area high on the shoreline where winter storms occasionally blow up large enough waves to create splash or spray. Animals that live in this region are exposed to air more than sea water and have adapted to cope with the extremes of the weather. The periwinkle is a spray zone inhabitant.

High intertidal zone

The high intertidal zone is covered with sea water only when tides are at their highest. Like the creatures that inhabit the spray zone, animals of the high intertidal zone are exposed daily to the open air and must tolerate the extremes of the seasons and retain moisture for a substantial period of time. The barnacle is a high intertidal zone inhabitant.

Middle intertidal zone

While the middle intertidal zone may be exposed daily to the air for a short time, it is usually covered with sea water. More marine animals live here than in the two higher regions of the shore. Middle intertidal zone inhabitants are the limpet, whelk, and hermit crab.

Low intertidal zone

The low intertidal zone is rarely exposed to the air except when it is experiencing the lowest of low tides. More animals live here than in all of the above-mentioned zones. Most marine animals and plants compete for low intertidal space. Low intertidal zone inhabitants include certain species of sea anemone and nudibranch.

Subtidal region

The subtidal region, as the name suggests, is not a part of the intertidal region. It is the area below the lowest tidal waters and is never exposed to the air.

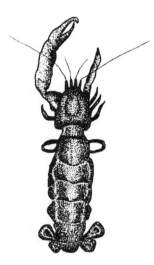

Ghost Shrimp: A High To Low Intertidal Zone Inhabitant Of Sandy/Muddy Beaches

17

How Do Intertidal Animals Move?

Intertidal animals use a variety of methods to move about to find food or a mate. Many species are not mobile and food is obtained from the sea water in which they are immersed.

Attached or sessile animals

Sessile animals are attached to hard surfaces, such as rocks, driftwood, along dock edges, and on other animals and plants. Sessile animals, such as the barnacle and oyster, are permanently attached and cannot move, while some attached animals, such as the sea anemone, can move, but do so very slowly.

Burrowers

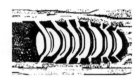

Burrowers dig by physical force or eat their way through a soft surface. Several species of segmented worms as well as various clam species burrow into mud flats and sandy beaches while shipworms and gribbles burrow through driftwood.

Crawlers

The limpet and moon snail are crawlers that maneuver around on a muscular foot. The crab gets around on jointed legs, while the sea star crawls with tube feet.

Drifters

Drifters drift about with the currents and tide. Jellyfish, the comb jelly and many invertebrate larvae are examples of drifters.

Swimmers

Swimmers are capable of actually stroking through the water. Fish that enter intertidal waters, typically to find food or to spawn, are swimmers, as are some marine segmented worms that are equipped with specialized swimming appendages called parapodia.

How Do Intertidal Animals Breathe?

Although it is a popular misconception, marine animals do not absorb the oxygen from water molecules: the O out of the H_2O as it were.

Breathe dissolved oxygen

Both land and marine animals must absorb oxygen and release carbon dioxide in order to live. The oxygen (O_2) marine animals breathe has been dissolved in or blended with sea water.

Oxygen from the Earth's atmosphere is transferred into the ocean's waters by the action of the wind over surface waters. As well, floating and rooted marine plants and microscopic phytoplankton near the water surface release oxygen into the water as a by-product of photosynthesis.

Breathing organs can take many shapes

Many small marine invertebrates absorb dissolved oxygen through diffusion over the entire surfaces of their bodies, while larger, more complex marine animals have developed specialized organs such as gills, to absorb dissolved oxygen.

Breathing organs can take on many shapes and sizes and can be located on the inside or outside of an animal's body.

Dual purpose respiratory organs

Many marine animals have dual-purpose respiratory organs. Not only are these organs used in breathing, but they are also used as sieves in the feeding process. For example, a bivalve like the clam, filters out microscopic plankton from the sea water travelling over its grate-like gills and passes the food to its mouth using cilia and mucous.

Did you know that... many species of sea cucumbers breathe through their anuses? Respiratory gills are internal and extend almost the entire length of their bodies. They draw in sea water through the anal opening, bathe the gills and then expel out the used water.

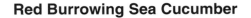

Red Burrowing Sea Cucumber

How Do Intertidal Animals Eat?

Filter or suspension feeders

Feeding Barnacle

These animals strain food from the water and direct it towards their mouths. They have special appendages or techniques to accomplish this.

In some, branched appendages fan the water toward the mouth or catch food on a sticky substance secreted on appendages that are exposed to the open water currents (barnacle). In others, incredibly fine hair-like filaments called cilia move in precise strokes to draw in a water current toward the mouth. This method of filter feeding is referred to as ciliary feeding (oyster, mussel).

Surface or deposit feeders

These animals sweep up deposits of detritus from the surface. In some, tentacles sweep the surrounding surface bottom and transport caught food into the mouth (sea cucumber). Siphons provide various clam species with access to the water while buried in sand or mud.

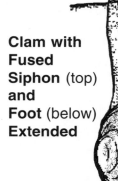

Clam with Fused Siphon (top) **and Foot** (below) **Extended**

Scraping or snaring feeders

Mollusk Radula

Some animals have a radula, a ribbon of tiny teeth that act like a grater. The radula either scrapes surface layers of cells off algae or drills through the shells of mollusks to reach the meat inside (limpet, whelk).

Others have a proboscis, a tubelike structure that the animal uses to either wrap around its prey like a lasso, or to inject toxins into its victim (nemertean worm).

Reproduction and Intertidal Animals

The sexual and asexual reproductive habits of marine invertebrates found in the intertidal region are exceedingly diverse.

Asexual reproduction

Asexual reproduction is usually the cloning or replication of genetically identical offspring. Marine invertebrate animals that reproduce asexually do so usually by budding (colonial sea squirts) or by shedding body parts that regenerate into new animals (sea anemone).

Sexual reproduction

In sexual reproduction, two parents are usually required, but not absolutely necessary. A single individual can be both male and female, otherwise known as a hermaphrodite, but most do not self-fertilize. Some intertidal animals copulate (whelks, crabs), but many marine invertebrates reproduce through broadcast fertilization.

Broadcast fertilization

Male and female gametes are shed into the surrounding sea water where fertilization occurs by chance (clams, worms). Species spawn according to a host of environmental factors, some of which are the phases of the moon and the consequential tidal effects, the amount of daily sunlight, and the increase of sea water temperature. Some species spawn in a phenomena called epidemic spawning whereby an individual begins the broadcasting process and the others automatically do the same.

Larval dispersal of intertidal animals

The vast majority of marine intertidal animals have a complex life cycle, whereby fertilized eggs hatch into a larvae stage that bears little resemblance to the adult. The larvae of these invertebrates typically drift in the water. This drifting larval stage greatly increases the dispersal of intertidal animals along the shoreline and the likelihood that new suitable substrate will be colonized. Once settled, a spectacular larval to adult metamorphosis occurs.

Did you know that...
the barnacle has a very long penis in relation to its body size? The hermaphrodite must extend its male organ into the mantle of its neighbour where sperm and eggs can mix.

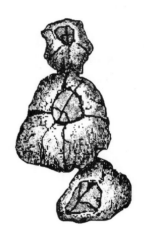

Acorn Barnacle

Intertidal Ecosystems

Ecology is the scientific study of factors that determine the distribution and abundance of plants and animals. Seashore ecologists examine the complex and diverse ways in which intertidal inhabitants interact with one another and with their environment.

Predation

An important seashore ecological field study conducted in the early 1960s demonstrated the co-dependency of all intertidal inhabitants. Ecologist Robert L. Paine established a study area along the Pacific shoreline and counted the number and variety of species living within its borders. He then removed the predatory Purple Sea Star, *Pisaster ochraceus* from the study area.

Paine discovered that the number of species living in the study area decreased over time. Without the constraint of the predatory sea star, the mussel population flourished, leaving little substrate space for other species to become established.

**Purple Sea Star,
*Pisaster
ochraceus***

Based on this study, Paine coined the term "keystone predator," an expression used to describe a predator that has an overwhelming impact on the abundance and diversity of other members of an ecological community.

Competition

What eats what is a major starting point in understanding the influence of predation and competition on the ecology of the shoreline. When exploring the seashore, take note of what an animal is eating. Is it a herbivore or carnivore? What method of eating is it using (filter feeding, scraping feeding?)

Consider what other species may be competing for the same food or substrate space. Competition exists between members of the same species and between two different species. Ecologists have observed that the more similar two species are in their ecological requirements, the more intense the competition.

These competitive interactions play important roles in explaining the distribution and abundance of intertidal plants and animals.

Intertidal Symbiotic Relationships

Symbiosis is used to describe any two organisms that live together. Ecologists recognize three different types of symbiotic interactions or partnerships that exist between intertidal plants and animals.

Mutualistic relationships

Mutualism is a symbiosis in which the two partners are metabolically dependent upon one another. The association between the Aggregating Sea Anemone, *Anthopleura elegantissima* and a microscopic single-celled algae called zooxanthellae is a good example of intertidal mutualism. The green and brown-coloured algae lives inside the anemone. As the algae photosynthesize and asexually reproduce, excess sugars are passed as food to the anemone. In turn, the anemone passes waste products to the algae which enables the algae to continue to grow.

Commensal relationships

Other animals have a more or less neutral or commensal relationship whereby one or both animals obtain food or protection from the other. The tiny pea crab, *Pinnixa subquadrata*, for example, finds protection by living inside the shells of a clam. Some scientists argue that the pea crab may be ingesting the clam's tissue as well as sharing its filtered water. If this is true, then the pea crab would be considered a parasite.

Parasitic relationships

Parasitism is a type of symbiotic intereaction whereby one partner lives at the expense of its host. The parasite partner is metabolically dependent upons its host and causes some degree of harm. Parasites can cause a variety of negative effects on its host such as behavioural changes, castration and increased mortality. Most parasites are invisible but very common components of intertidal ecosystems.

Did you know that...
an awareness of the complex ecological interactions between plants and animals can enrich a trip to the beach? One soon begins to appreciate that there is more to seashore exploring than simply identifying animals and plants.

Seaweeds

It would be impossible to go to the seashore and not wonder as much about the marine plants as the animals living there. Searching for intertidal creatures involves poking about in and under seaweed; so much of it is amazingly colourful and textured.

Seaweeds or algae (pronounced [AL-jee] which is the plural, alga [al-guh] is singular) range in size from microscopic one-celled diatoms to massive kelps that grow to a height of thirty metres.

Holdfast, stipe and blade

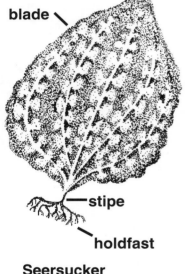

blade

stipe

holdfast

Seersucker

Algae are very different from terrestrial plants. Seaweeds do not have a vascular system that carries nutrients up from the roots, through the stem to the leaves of the plant. Algae derive energy from the sun and nutrients from sea water which are absorbed by cells all over the algal surface. What appears to be a rootlike structure is the holdfast which is used to attach to a substrate. It varies in size according to species and can be small and disc-shaped or large and branched. The stipe is the stemlike structure that usually keeps the leaflike structure or the blade near the water's surface so photosynthesis can occur. In many species of seaweeds, the blade grows from the base of the algae near the stipe. If a blade is torn or ripped off, a new blade will grow, as long as the holdfast and stipe remain.

Depending upon the species, algae can be annual or perennial. During winter storms, the stipes and blades of many species are torn away, but the holdfast remains and the seaweed regrows in the spring.

How does algae reproduce?

Algal reproduction is a complex process which varies according to species. Many species reproduce in a process called alternation of generations. The first generation reproduces sexually by shedding gametes into the water. The second generation reproduces asexually through the release of spores. The third generation reproduces sexually and the cycle continues.

Intertidal zonation and seaweed

Like intertidal animals, different species of algae grow on various bottoms or substrates and in distinct zones up and down the intertidal region. Some algae are able to tolerate exposure to the sunlight more than others and can be found growing higher up in the intertidal region. Other algae are definite shade plants, while still others are very particular about the salinity of the sea water in which they grow.

Three major phyla

Classified into three major phyla, seaweed are grouped, in general, according to their colour. All algae contain green-coloured chlorophyll necessary for photosynthesis to take place; however, other pigments contained within the seaweed often mask the green pigment.

Green Algae or Phylum Chlorophyta

In general, green algae require plenty of light and tend to grow in the higher intertidal region or in shallow subtidal water. (Sea Lettuce, *Ulva sp.* and Green String Lettuce, *Enteromorpha linza*).

Sea Lettuce

Brown Algae or Phylum Phaetophyta

Sometimes referred to as kelp, many species of brown algae have pneumatocysts. These hollow gas filled floats help keep the plant afloat near the surface of the water to ensure that enough sunlight is absorbed for photosynthesis (Bull Kelp, *Nereocystis leutkeana* and Rockweed, *Fucus sp.*).

Rockweed

Red Algae or Phylum Rhodophyta

Mostly filamentous or sheet-like, red algae produce a starch known as carrageenan or agar as a by-product of photosynthesis. Check on the ingredients label of many ice creams and puddings and you will see that carrageenan is often listed as a jelling agent and stabilizer (Red Dulse, *Porphyra perforata*).

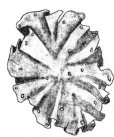

Red Dulse

Seaweed as a source of food and habitat

Marine plants are a major food source for many intertidal herbivores. Moreover, the holdfasts and fronds of algae are receptacles for all sorts of organic material. From rotting seaweed to decaying animals, this detritus stays suspended near and on the seaweed so that many non-herbivorous animals either eat it or eat the animals that forage on the organic matter.

Habitat for many intertidal creatures is provided by marine plants. During low tide, many animals use the seaweed as a refuge to hide under in order to escape exposure to the direct sunlight and open air conditions.

Did you know that...
plankton includes all of the drifting life of the ocean, from the smallest microscopic organism to the largest jellyfish? Plankton represents the greatest mass of life on Earth.

Phytoplankton and zooplankton

Although microscopic plants or phytoplankton [fie-toe-PLANK-ton] are invisible to the seashore explorer's eye, they and microscopic animals called zooplankton [zoe-PLANK-ton] play a very important role in the intertidal community. Microscopic phytoplankton are the foundation of marine food webs or chains .

Zooplankton, which also include marine invertebrate eggs and larvae, eat phytoplankton or other zooplankton in order to survive. Phytoplankton, like other algae, produce their own food by photosynthesis.

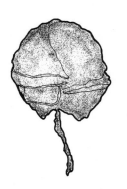

Microscopic Phytoplankton *Alexandrium sp.*

Major producers of oxygen

As a by-product of the phytoplankton's photosynthetic process, oxygen is released into the sea water. Not only is this oxygen used by marine animals to breathe, it has been estimated that eighty per cent of the oxygen in our atmosphere is produced by phytoplankton.

The largest concentration of phytoplankton along the east coast of Vancouver Island occurs during the spring when nutrients in the sea water are replenished by fresh water runoff from winter rains and snow. Excessive growths can produce what is commonly called "red tide" or "harmful algal bloom." When this occurs, Paralytic Shellfish Poisoning is of great danger to shellfish harvesters. This topic is discussed in the chapter on "Mud Flats."

COMMUNITY AND PROVINCIAL PARKS WITH BEACH ACCESS

Beach access

In general, all lands between the tides are Canadian Crown Land and are, therefore, publicly owned. Land above the high tide line can be privately owned and seashore explorers should respect the privacy of ocean front properties.

In residential areas, public access to the shoreline is often designated by "Beach Access" signs clearly posted on streets. Foot paths and stairways lead directly to the beach.

Provincial parks

Provincial parks with beach access are indicated on most highway maps. Also available from tourist information centres and BC Park Offices is a map called, *"Provincial Parks of Vancouver Island."*

Most provincial parks have picnic, rest room and camping/recreational vehicle facilities. Marine coastal parks provide mooring buoys and landing floats for boaters.

Entrances or access roads to provincial parks are indicated from major highways on Vancouver Island by large blue and white signs that provide the park name and list, in symbols, the major facilities available.

Information shelters are located at the entrances of most provincial parks. These notice boards provide maps of the park, indicate trail routes and campgrounds, and advise park visitors of any wildlife sightings, shellfish harvesting restrictions or other regulations to be observed.

It should be noted that dogs are not allowed on beaches in provincial parks.

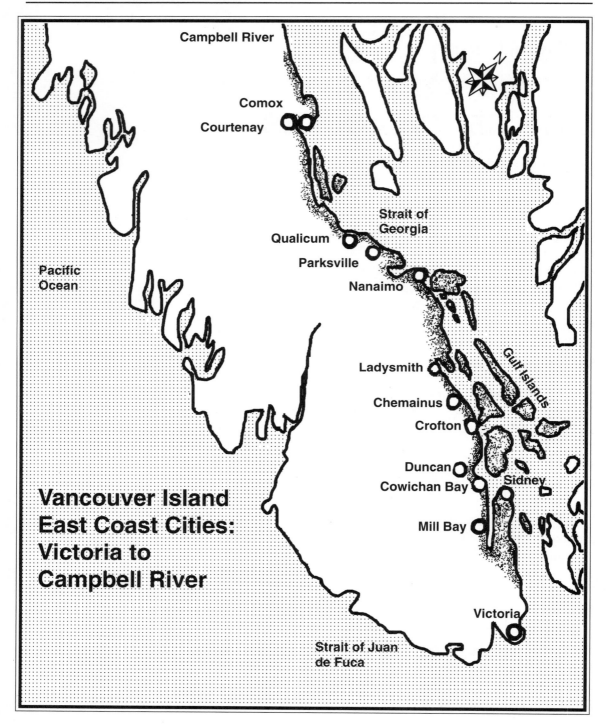

Campbell River

Comox

Courtenay

Strait of
Georgia

Qualicum

Parksville

Nanaimo

Pacific
Ocean

Ladysmith

Chemainus

Crofton

Gulf Islands

Duncan

Cowichan Bay

Sidney

Mill Bay

Vancouver Island
East Coast Cities:
Victoria to
Campbell River

Victoria

Strait of Juan
de Fuca

Visitor centres

Many provincial parks have visitor centres that provide local natural history information. Free interpretative programs, such as low tide beach walks, are regularly scheduled throughout the summer months. Printed guides and schedules of the programs are available through the BC Parks Offices.

Regional and community parks

In general, regional or community parks offer fewer facilities than do provincial parks. Picnic and rest room facilities are usually available. Regional parks do not provide camping or overnight facilities and are restricted to day use only, usually from dawn to dusk.

Many of the community parks are difficult for the newcomer or tourist to find since so few are indicated by signs from major highways or roads. Most of the regional and community parks are shown on community municipal maps available from local tourist information centres.

Parks grouped into six geographic areas

The provincial and regional parks along the east coast of the Island have been divided into six geographic areas:

- **Victoria/Saanich Peninsula**
- **Gulf Islands**
- **Duncan/Cowichan**
- **Ladysmith/Nanaimo**
- **Parksville/Qualicum**
- **Comox/Courtenay**

Park beach type and facilities

The predominate beach type or substrate of each park is described but seashore explorers should be aware that many parks have a variety of substrates. Rest room, picnic, camping, playground, and trail facilities are also listed. Road directions to each park are provided from major highways.

Did you know that...
a small island in Nanaimo's Departure Bay was instrumental in the development of a world-wide intertidal zonation scheme? In the 1950s, biologists T.A. and Anne Stephenson, working out of the Pacific Biological Station, published an important research paper about the intertidal animal and plant zonation of Brandon Island.

29

Public wharves and floating docks

Most east coast communities have government-owned wharves or floating docks that are accessible by the public. Listed here are a few of the harbours and towns with public wharves:

Victoria/Saanich Peninsula:
- Sidney
- Shoal Harbour
- Swartz Bay
- Brentwood Bay

Gulf Islands:
- Fulford Harbour (Saltspring Island)
- Ganges (Saltspring Island)
- Montague Harbour (Galiano Island)
- Degnen Bay (Gabriola Island)
- Ford Cove (Hornby Island)

Duncan/Cowichan:
- Mill Bay
- Cowichan Bay
- Crofton
- Chemainus

Ladysmith/Nanaimo:
- Ladysmith
- Nanaimo Commercial Inlet
- Newcastle Island's Mark Bay

Comox/Courtenay:
- Deep Bay
- Fanny Bay
- Buckley Bay
- Union Bay
- Comox.

Victoria/
Saanich Peninsula

Mt. Douglas Municipal Park

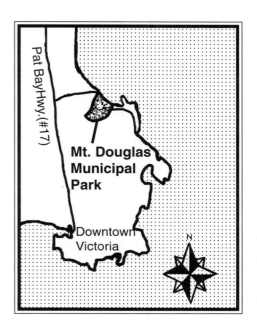

Beach type: mixed mud, clay, sand, gravel
Closest community: Victoria
Directions: From Pat Bay Highway (#17), turn east on Royal Oak Drive and proceed east on Cordova Bay Road to park entrance.
Facilities: picnic, rest room
Administered by: Capital Regional District Parks
Notes: A short trail through the forest leads to steps or a very steep path to the beach. Freshwater stream enters Strait on beach.

Island View Regional Park

Beach type: mixed sand and gravel
Closest community: between Sidney and Victoria on the east side of Saanich Peninsula
Directions: From Pat Bay Highway (#17), turn east onto Island View Road. Turn north on Homathko Drive.
Facilities: picnic, rest room
Administered by: Capital Regional District Parks
Notes: It is possible to walk to the south along beach to Mt. Douglas Municipal Park.

Tslip Park (Sidney)

Beach type: mixed sand and gravel
Closest community: in Sidney
Directions: From Pat Bay Highway (#17), turn east on Lochside Drive. (Or follow Washington State Ferries, Sidney - Anacortes Ferry signs.) Park is south of Ferry Terminal.
Facilities: sheltered picnic, rest room, children's playground
Administered by: Capital Regional District Parks
Notes: The beach is hidden behind a sandstone breakwater that was built to protect the shore from the Ferry's wake.

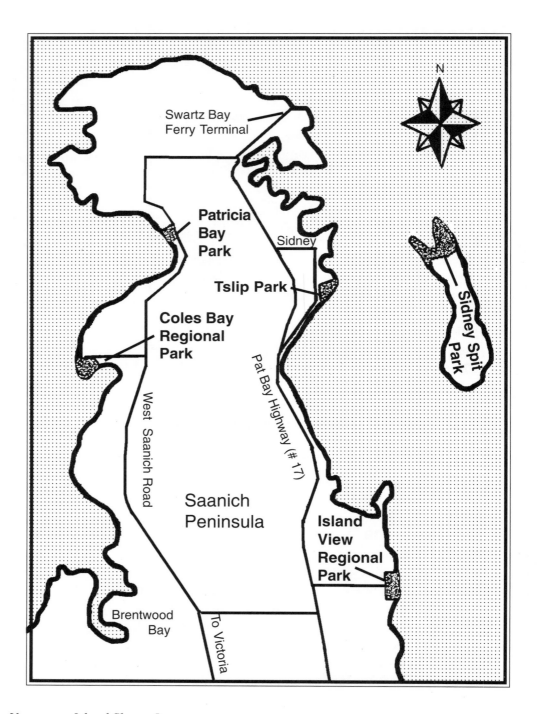

Sidney Spit Provincial Marine Park

Beach type: sandy tidal flats
Closest community: 5 kilometres (3 miles) offshore of Sidney
Directions: Accessible by privately owned passenger ferry service from the middle of May to the end of September. The Sidney Island Ferry departs from the Port of Sidney Marina.
Facilities: camping, picnic, rest room, children's playground, summer interpretative programs
Administered by: BC Parks South Vancouver Island Office
Notes: This popular marine park has shallow sandy beaches that are very popular with swimmers.

Patricia Bay Park

Beach type: gravel and cobblestone with sand
Closest community: Sidney
Directions: From Pat Bay Highway (#17), turn west on McTavish Road. Proceed north on West Saanich Road. The park is just north of the Fisheries and Oceans Institute of Ocean Sciences (9860 West Saanich Road).
Facilities: picnic, rest room
Administered by: Capital Regional District Parks
Notes: As a tidal flat, the gentle grade and warm waters in the summer time make it a favourite for swimming.

Coles Bay Regional Park

Beach type: sand, mud and gravel
Closest community: Brentwood Bay
Directions: From Pat Bay Highway (#17), turn west on McTavish Road. Turn north on West Saanich Road and west on Ardmore Drive. Proceed south on Inverness Road to park entrance.
Facilities: picnic, rest room, nature trails
Administered by: Capital Regional District Parks
Notes: A short trail from the parking lot leads to the beach. Outcrops of igneous rock are of interest to local geologists.

Gulf Islands

Saltspring Island

Saltspring Island can be reached by BC Ferries from Tsawwassen Ferry Terminal to Long Harbour (near Ganges), from Swartz Bay (Victoria) Ferry Terminal to Fulford Harbour, and from Crofton Ferry Terminal to Vesuvius Bay.

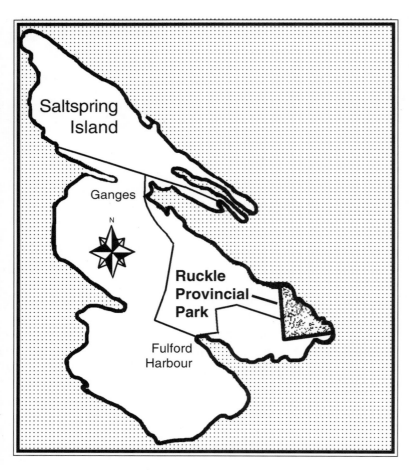

Ruckle Provincial Park

Beach type: gravel, cobblestone and rocky

Directions: From Fulford Harbour Ferry Terminal, turn north on Beaver Point Road and proceed directly to park. From Long Harbour Ferry Terminal, proceed on Long Harbour Road, turn south on Fulford Ganges Road and turn north on Beaver Point Road.

Facilities: camping (on shoreline), picnic, rest room, nature trails, summer interpretative programs

Administered by: BC Parks

Notes: There are almost 8 kilometres (5 miles) of shoreline.

Galiano Island

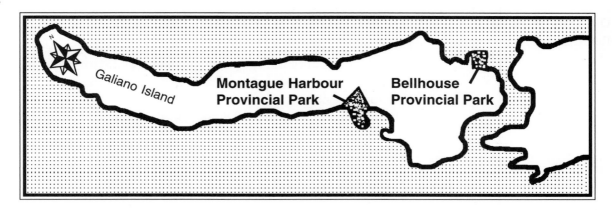

Montague Harbour Marine Provincial Park

Beach type: sand, gravel and rocks to the north and west
Directions: Take Montague Harbour Road west to Porlier Pass Road.
Facilities: camping, picnic, rest room, summer interpretative programs, boat ramp, dock and anchorage facilities
Administered by: BC Parks
Notes: Floating Nature House is a converted boat house that offers a variety of summer interpretative programs.

Bellhouse Provincial Park

Beach type: sand, gravel and rocks to the north and west
Directions: From Sturdies Bay Ferry Terminal, take Burrill Road to the south and turn east into park entrance.
Facilities: picnic, rest room
Administered by: BC Parks

Gabriola Island

Access to the island is by a 20 minute BC Ferry trip from downtown Nanaimo (across from the Harbour Park Mall).

Malaspina Galleries Regional Park

Did you know that...
European drawings of the Malaspina Galleries were first made in the 1790s by Spanish explorers?

Beach type: sandstone
Directions: From Ferry Terminal, turn north at Taylor Bay Road. Turn west at Malaspina Drive to the end of the road.
Facilities: none
Administered by: Regional District of Nanaimo
Notes: The unique sandstone galleries, carved by water and wind, are 100 metres (330 feet) long.

Gabriola Sands Provincial Park

Beach type: gravel and sand with rocks (sandstone)
Directions: From Ferry Terminal, turn north at Taylor Bay Road. Turn east on Berry Point Road and turn north onto Ricardo Road.
Facilities: picnic, rest room, children's playground
Administered by: BC Parks
Notes: Also known as Twin Beaches, Taylor Bay and Pilot Bay are separated by the road. Parking for either beach is available on the east side of Ricardo Road.

Drumbeg Provincial Park

Beach type: gravel and sand with rocks (sandstone)
Directions: From Ferry Terminal, take North or South Road west. Turn west on Coast Road and northeast onto Stalker Road.
Facilities: rest room
Administered by: BC Parks
Notes: A dirt road into the park leads directly to a parking lot beside a small gravel beach.

Gabriola Island

Sandwell Provincial Park

Beach type: sand and rocks (sandstone)

Directions: From Ferry Terminal, take North Road west. Turn
north on Barret Road, north again on Bluewater Road and turn
west onto Strand Road. Parking at the end of the road.

Facilities: rest room, picnic

Administered by: BC Parks

Notes: To get to the beach, visitors must walk for fifteen
minutes along a forest path. The trail drops very steeply to a
grey sand beach. To the north and south, it is mixed with
gravel and sandstone boulders. Fairly secluded.

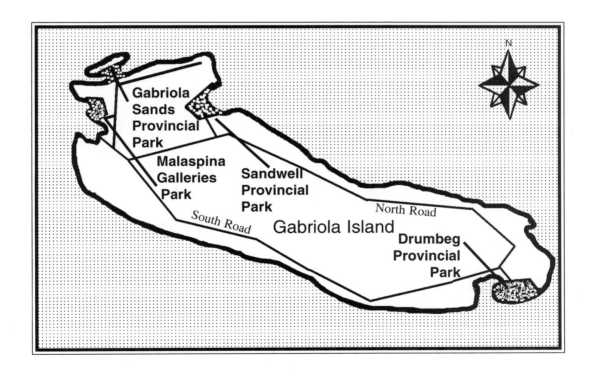

Denman and Hornby Islands

Both islands are accessible by automobile ferry year round from the Buckley Bay terminal, located south of Courtenay. Hornby Island is accessible from Gravelly Bay terminal on Denman Island.

Helliwell Provincial Park (Hornby Island)

Beach type: gravel and sandstone

Directions: From Central Road, turn north on St. John Point Road. Proceed to park entrance.

Facilities: picnic, rest room, nature trails

Administered by: BC Parks Strathcona District

Notes: To the northeast are gravel and sandstone beaches. To the south, the Helliwell Bluffs provide a spectacular view of the Strait.

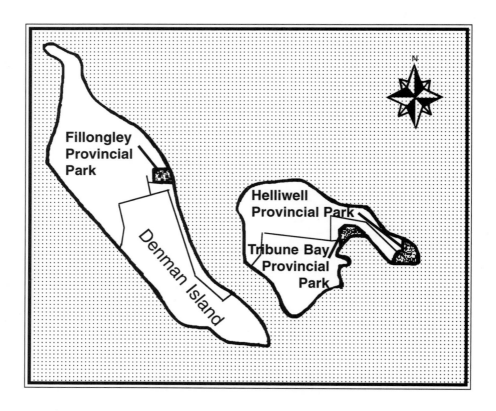

Tribune Bay Provincial Park (Hornby Island)

Beach type: sand, sandstone
Directions: From Ferry Terminal, take Central Road east.
Facilities: picnic, rest room, nature trails
Administered by: BC Parks Strathcona District
Notes: About one kilometre (.6 miles) of sandy beach.

Fillongley Provincial Park (Denman Island)

Beach type: sand
Directions: From Denman Road, turn north onto Swan Road.
Turn east at Beadnell Road to park entrance.
Facilities: camping, rest room, picnic
Administered by: BC Parks Strathcona District
Notes: Popular with swimmers and shellfish harvesters.

Cowichan/Duncan

Hecate Park

Beach type: mud tidal flats
Closest community:
Cowichan Bay
Directions: From Trans
Canada Highway (#1), turn
east onto Cowichan Bay
Road. Proceed southeast to
park.
Facilities: picnic only
Administered by: North
Cowichan Regional District
Notes: Parking facilities to
the north of Cowichan Bay
Road.

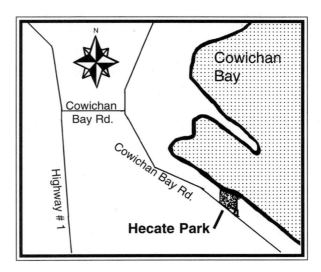

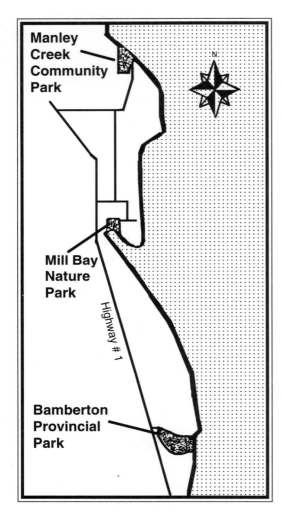

Manley Creek Community Park

Beach type: sand/mud mixed with cobblestone
Closest community: Cobble Hill
Directions: From Trans Canada Highway (#1), turn east onto Hutchinson Road. Turn north on Ratcliffe Road and proceed to the end of road.
Facilities: picnic and rest room
Administered by: North Cowichan Regional District
Notes: Parking facilities at road, bark path follows the creek down to picnic area and lookout. Proceed on steep dirt path to beach.

Mill Bay Nature Park

Beach type: mud/sand with gravel foreshore
Closest community: Mill Bay
Directions: From Trans Canada Highway (#1), turn east onto Kilmalu Road. Proceed south and turn west onto Holling Road.
Facilities: rest room, nature trails
Administered by: South Cowichan Regional District
Notes: Parking and facilities are not at beach. Gravel road and wooden steps lead to the shore.

Bamberton Provincial Park

Beach type: sand and gravel
Closest community: Mill Bay
Directions: From Trans Canada Highway (#1), turn east onto Mill Bay Road.
Facilities: camping, picnic, rest room, nature trails
Administered by: BC Parks South Vancouver Island District
Notes: Steps and paved trail (for wheelchair access) leads down a fairly steep incline to the shoreline. Camping facilities are located well away from the beach.

Kin Park Chemainus

Beach type: gravel and sand

Closest community: Chemainus

Directions: From Trans Canada Highway (#1), turn east onto River or Henry Road. Turn north on Chemainus Road. Turn east on Pine Street and north on Willow Street.

Facilities: picnic, rest room, children's playground

Administered by: North Cowichan Regional District

Notes: A boat ramp is located directly to the east of the park.

Crofton Beach Park

Beach type: sandy

Closest community: Crofton

Directions: From Trans Canada Highway (#1), turn east on Westholme Road, east on Crofton Road, east on Chaplin Street, south at York Avenue, east at Adelaide Street and turn north at Berridge Street.

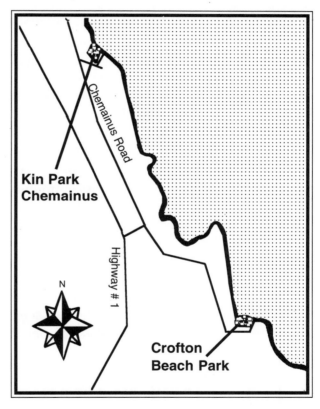

Facilities: picnic, rest room

Administered by: North Cowichan Regional District

Notes: Beach is in full view of the Crofton pulp and paper mill. Parking is provided at the end of the street on an open field, and access is a rather steep incline down a grassy path to the beach.

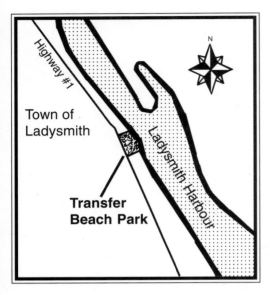

Town of Ladysmith

Transfer Beach Park

Highway #1

Ladysmith Harbour

Ladysmith/Nanaimo

Transfer Beach Park
Beach type: gravel, cobblestone with sand
Closest community: in Ladysmith
Directions: From Trans Canada Highway (#1), turn east onto Oyster Cove Road.
Facilities: sheltered picnic, rest room, children's playground
Administered by: Ladysmith Chamber of Commerce
Notes: Parking facilities are close to the beach and picnic area.

Roberts Memorial Provincial Park
Beach type: rocky (sandstone)
Closest community: twenty kilometres south of Nanaimo
Directions: From Trans Canada Highway (#1), turn east onto Cedar Road. Turn east onto Yellow Point Road.
Facilities: picnic
Administered by: BC Parks
Notes: It is a fifteen-minute walk from the parking lot to the sandstone beach.

Maffeo Sutton Park
Beach type: sandy, gravel, docks
Closest community: in Nanaimo
Directions: Near the Civic Arena, corner of Comox Road and Trans Canada Highway #1 (Terminal Avenue.)
Facilities: picnic, rest room, children's playground
Administered by: Regional District of Nanaimo
Notes: The artificial Swy-a-lana Lagoon provides swimming in summer months.

To Nanaimo

Yellowpoint Rd.

Roberts Memorial Provincial Park

Neck Point Park

Beach type: gravel/cobblestone and rocky

Closest community: in Nanaimo

Directions: From Island Highway (#19), turn east on Departure Bay Road, then east again on Hammond Bay Road. Turn north at Morningside Drive.

Facilities: trails

Administered by: Regional District of Nanaimo

Notes: Rocky headlands.

Piper's Lagoon Park

Beach type: sand/gravel and rocky

Closest community: in Nanaimo

Directions: From Island Highway (#19), turn east on Departure Bay Road, then east again on Hammond Bay Road. Turn east at Lagoon Road and south onto Place Road to park entrance.

Facilities: picnic, rest room, trails

Administered by: Regional District of Nanaimo

Notes: A sandy/gravel spit extends out to rocky headlands.

Newcastle Island Marine Park

Beach type: sandstone, gravel

Closest community: Nanaimo

Directions: Foot-passenger ferry departs from Maffeo Sutton Park

Facilities: picnic, camping, Visitors' Centre, nature trails

Administered by: BC Parks, South Vancouver Island District

Notes: Summer programs. Ferry service from May to October.

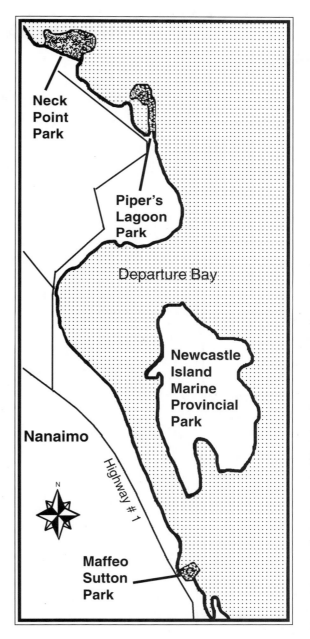

Parksville/Qualicum

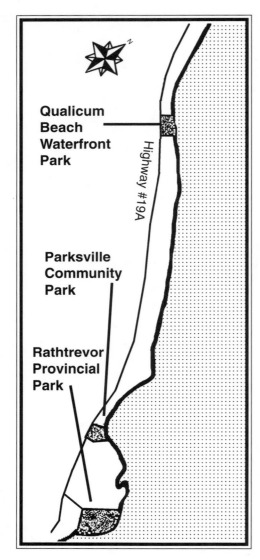

Qualicum Beach Waterfront Park

Beach type: gravel
Closest community: in Qualicum Beach
Directions: From Highway #19A, park along highway north of Memorial Avenue.
Facilities: picnic, benches
Administered by: Qualicum Beach
Notes: Side-walk runs along the beach near Tourist Information Centre.

Parksville Community Park

Beach type: sandy
Closest community: in Parksville
Directions: From Highway #19A, turn east onto Corfield Street, and north at Beach Side Drive.
Facilities: picnic, rest room, children's playground and water park, snack bar
Administered by: Community of Parksville
Notes: The park and children's playground area is one of the most pleasant on the east coast. The long meandering sandy beach is popular with swimmers.

Rathtrevor Beach Provincial Park

Beach type: sandy
Closest community: 1.5 kilometres south of Parksville
Directions: From Highway #19A, turn east directly into park.
Facilities: camping, picnic, rest room, Visitors' Centre, summer interpretative programs
Administered by: BC Parks (Parksville Office)
Notes: The popularity of the park is undoubtedly due to the wonderful sandy beach and warm water of Northwest Bay.

Comox/Courtenay

Goose Spit Regional Park

Beach type: mud flats and sandy
Closest community: in Comox
Directions: From Island Highway (#19), turn east onto Comox Road. Turn north at Pritchard Road and east onto Hawkins Road.
Facilities: picnic, rest room
Administered by: Comox Valley Chamber of Commerce
Notes: Parking is available on the east and west sides of the road.

Kye Bay Beach Elks Park

Beach type: sand
Closest community: Comox
Directions: From Island Highway (#19), turn east onto Comox Road. Proceed to Lazo Road and follow Kye Bay Road to park.
Facilities: picnic, rest room
Administered by: Elks Lodge No. 60
Notes: Extensive sandy beach is popular with swimmers.

Kin Beach Class C Provincial Park

Beach type: cobblestone and gravel
Closest community: Comox
Directions: From Island Highway (#19), turn east onto Ryan Road. Turn north at Military Road, then proceed east on Kilmorley Road to Astra Road
Facilities: camping (no hook-ups), rest room, picnic, store in summer months
Administered by: Grant and Ann Hamilton, Park Managers
Notes: There are no signs indicating the location of this park which is open all year round. Site of endangered flower species along foreshore.

Seal Bay Nature Regional Park

Beach type: cobblestone and gravel
Closest community: Comox
Directions: From Island Highway (#19), turn east on Ryan Road, north on Anderton Road, which turns into Waveland Road. Turn north on Bates Road.
Facilities: rest room, nature trails
Administered by: Comox Valley Chamber of Commerce
Notes: It is a ten to fifteen-minute walk from the parking area along the side of Bates Road through a forest trail to the beach. Take the marked "Main Beach Access" path. Please note that the path is very steep just before reaching the beach.

Kitty Coleman Beach Provincial Park

Beach type: cobblestone and gravel
Closest community: Campbell River
Directions: From Island Highway (#19), turn east onto Coleman Road. Turn east onto Left Road and then take Whittaker Road south to the park.
Facilities: camping, picnic, rest room, boat ramp
Administered by: BC Parks Strathcona District, Miracle Beach Office
Notes: Cobblestone beach on the foreshore. Popular with boaters and fishers.

Miracle Beach Provincial Park

Beach type: sandy
Closest community: Campbell River
Directions: From Island Highway (#19), turn east onto Miracle Beach Drive.
Facilities: camping, picnic, rest room, nature trails, Visitors' Centre, summer interpretative programs
Administered by: BC Parks Strathcona District, Miracle Beach Office
Notes: Shallow water warms the sandy beach of Elma Bay, making it very popular with swimmers.

Comox/Courtenay Area
Provincial and Regional Parks

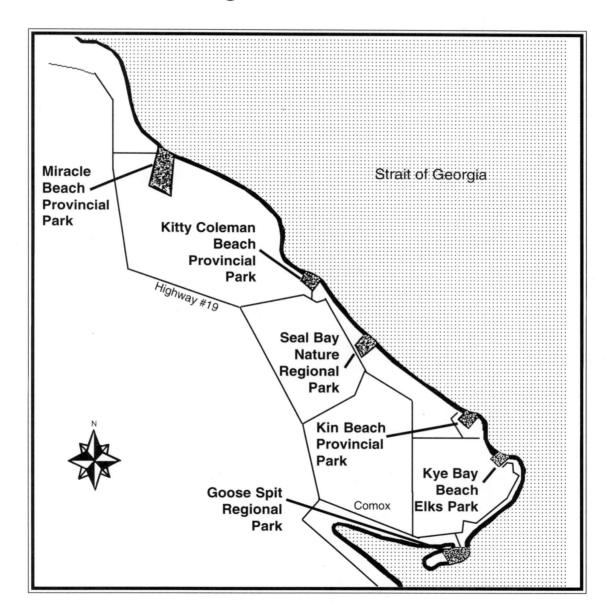

Miracle
Beach
Provincial
Park

Kitty Coleman
Beach
Provincial
Park

Highway #19

Strait of Georgia

Seal Bay
Nature
Regional
Park

Kin Beach
Provincial
Park

Kye Bay
Beach
Elks Park

N

Goose Spit
Regional
Park

Comox

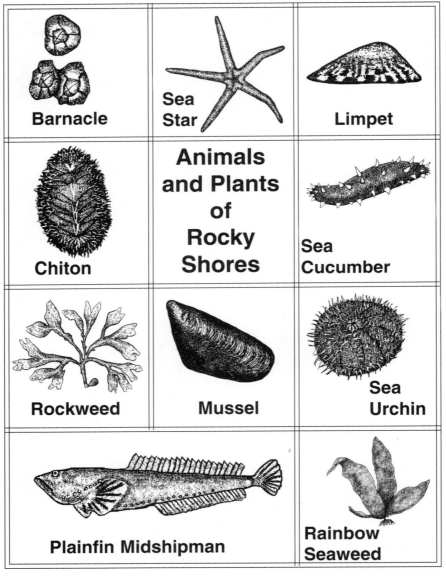

Barnacle	Sea Star	Limpet
Chiton	**Animals and Plants of Rocky Shores**	Sea Cucumber
Rockweed	Mussel	Sea Urchin
Plainfin Midshipman		Rainbow Seaweed

Vancouver Island Shores I

ROCKY SHORES
AND TIDEPOOLS

Life abounds on rocky shores. More varieties of marine plants and animals live here than on any other shore type found along the east coast of Vancouver Island.

Most of the animals encountered are attached to a rock surface either by cementing themselves to it or clinging to it by vacuum suction. Many seaweeds attach securely to the craggy surface of rocks and their fronds and holdfasts host a variety of animals and plants. To avoid direct sunlight, many nocturnal creatures hide deep in crevices on rocky shores while others, to preserve moisture, seek shelter in cracks during low tide.

Sandstone, shale and conglomerates

Rocky shorelines along the east coast of Vancouver Island consist primarily of large slabs of sandstone, shale and silt stone conglomerates. These sedimentary rocks were created by the consolidation of loose sediments that have been compressed into layers or strata. Sandstone, for example, is composed of layers of quartz sand, and shale is made predominantly of silt and clay particles.

Crevices and tidepools provide habitat

Sedimentary rocks are easily eroded by the powerful effects of tidal currents and storm waves. Sandstone sea cliffs, like those on Gabriola Island, have been cut into enormous galleries through which the seashore explorer can wander. More importantly, the erosive effect of water gouges deep crevices and tidepools on the east coast's rocky shores, providing a wealth of habitat for plant and animal life.

**On
Rocky Shores,
Look For**

1
Barnacle
2
Limpet
3
Sea Star
4
Chiton
5
Sea Cucumber
6
Sea Urchin
7
Fish
8
Rockweed
9
Sea Moss
10
**Rainbow
Seaweed**

Species and natural history of these creatures and plants are described in this chapter.

49

Tips for exploring rocky shores

✪   Look for paths of gravel and cobblestone, created by the continuous backwash of waves and tidal current, that lead down to low tide rocks.

✪   Avoid exploring vertical rocky cliffs. The risk of falling is too great.

✪   Steep rocky shores can be treacherous. Walk on all fours like a crab to maintain balance.

✪   Be cautious of rocks that are covered so thickly with seaweed that it may be impossible to see where a secure foothold can be found.

✪   Covering most rocks are barnacles that have a razor-like ability to cut into skin. Wear gardening gloves to protect your hands.

✪   Walking shoes or hiking boots with excellent ankle support and tread are highly recommended. Use a pair that you don't mind getting wet.

✪   Look for tidepools during low tide, where a variety of animals continue to go about their daily activities.

Parks with rocky shores

Listed here are a few of the parks with rocky shores along the Strait of Georgia. Refer to the chapter on "Parks With Beach Access" for a complete listing.

Coles Bay Regional Park Victoria/Saanich Peninsula
Neck Point Park Ladysmith/Nanaimo
Helliwell Provincial Park Hornby Island
Drumbeg Provincial Park Gabriola Island

More Animals To Look For On Rocky Shores

Mussel
Sea Anemone
Hermit Crab
Periwinkle
Whelk
Shore Crab

Species and natural history of these creatures are described in other chapters.

The Barnacle

The barnacle is probably the easiest creature to identify along our shores. These little volcano-shaped animals seem to be just about everywhere. Look on rock cliffs, small boulders, clam shells, pieces of driftwood and wharf pilings. They are crowded together from the high to the low tide line. It's rather amazing to see just how high up on the shoreline one can find barnacles.

Barnacle with Extended Cirri Appendages

High Intertidal Zone dwellers

How do they survive where high tide waters will only reach them a few times a month? The barnacle has a shell that is designed like a retractable-roofed sports dome. Triangular plates are the walls of the barnacle's conical-shaped dome, and hinged plates on the roof, called the operculum, are able to open and close. The barnacle is able to shut out the extremes of the weather as well as retain moisture inside its shell for long periods of time.

Inside the barnacle's shell, its internal organs are enclosed in a fleshy envelope called a mantle.

Barnacle Facts
Species: 750 world wide; 23 in Pacific Northwest
Phylum: Arthropoda
Reproduction: hermaphrodites that fertilize neighbour barnacle
Food: phytoplankton
Predators: whelks and sea stars
Life span: 3 to 5 years

Cirri appendages to eat and breathe

In order to eat and breathe, the barnacle extends feathery appendages called cirri up through the roof of its dome. By fanning the surrounding water, microscopic plankton are caught in the appendages' fine netting. The barnacle pulls the cirri back inside its dome and deposits the plankton near its mouth. At the same time, dissolved oxygen is absorbed over the surface of the cirri to facilitate breathing.

The cirri fan the surrounding sea water at an amazing rate of 80 to 100 times per minute. If water currents are strong when feeding, the barnacle needs only to hold out the cirri to net its food.

Kicking or fanning is not necessary. When the water current direction changes, the barnacle can rotate its cirri 180 degrees so that it can net as much food as possible.

Related to the crab

Did you know that...
when a barnacle larva selects a location to settle, it tests a site for the necessary number of centimetres needed for future growth? If other barnacles of the same species are too close, it searches for another location. If a smaller species is near, the larger barnacle ignores it, settles down and eventually overgrows or crushes its smaller neighbour.

Although the barnacle's shell-like plates would suggest it is related to the mollusk, the barnacle is a crustacean. Like most crustaceans, the barnacle moults its plates in order to grow.

Amazing mating behaviour

One of the most fascinating aspects of the barnacle's life is its mating behaviour. As hermaphrodites, barnacles possess both male and female reproductive organs. The barnacle has a very long penis in relation to its overall body size. The necessity for such a long appendage is obvious. It must extend its penis into the mantle of its neighbour where sperm and eggs can mix.

Larva settles down by standing on its head

A free-swimming larva is hatched from an egg that is brooded inside the parent. Once adrift in the sea water, it propels itself with its cirri that are used as feeding and breathing appendages in adulthood. The larva grows through various moults, deriving its nourishment from plankton. At around a quarter of a centimetre in length (the width of a grain of rice), the larva settles down and finds a permanent resting place. While standing on its head and using its antennae as suckers to stay in one place, the barnacle secretes a cement that permanently attaches it to a rock or other hard surface.

Tips for finding barnacles

✪ To get a close up view of the barnacle using its cirri appendages, bring a magnifying glass.

✪ Look for scar remnants from the barnacle plate rings left behind on rocks and shells. Barnacle cement is one of the strongest known natural glues.

Chthamalus dalli

[THAM-al-us DALL-ee]

Common name: Little Acorn Barnacle, Brown Buckshot Barnacle, Dall's Barnacle

Where: on any hard object in the intertidal zone: rocks, pilings, boulders, other animals with hard surfaces

Zone: high intertidal

Colour: brownish-grey

Shape: conical, low with flattened top, two pairs of plates overlapping that form a cross-shape when closed and two unpaired end plates

Size: up to .5 cm (.2 inches) wide at base and .4 cm (.15 inches) high

Note: This is the smallest barnacle on our coast. Often so dense, they literally blanket the rocks.

Balanus glandula

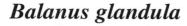

[BAHL-ann-us GLAND-you-la]

Common name: Acorn Barnacle

Where: on any hard object in the intertidal zone: rocks, pilings, boulders, other animals with hard surfaces

Zone: high intertidal

Colour: whitish grey

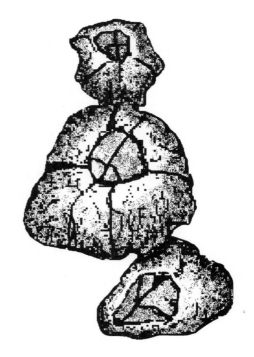

Shape: conical, low and broad with prominent ridges if not crowded together, flattened top, two pairs of plates overlapping two unpaired plates

Size: up to 1.5 cm (.6 inches) wide and 1 cm (.4 inches) high but can grow higher when in crowded conditions

Notes: Empty barnacle shells are often found washed up on shorelines.

The Limpet

The limpet is a small, cone-shaped shelled mollusk that is easily overlooked by the seashore explorer. It seeks refuge under shady rock ledges or deep in crevices during low tide, away from direct sunlight and the seashore explorer's eyes.

Limpet Facts
Species: 30 in Pacific Northwest
Phylum: Mollusca, Class Gastropoda
Reproduction: broadcast fertilizer
Food: scrapes algae off rocks with radula
Predators: shore birds, sea stars
Life span: 5 to 16 years

Powerful suction foot

The limpet is a gastropod (see chapter on "Gravel and Cobblestone Beaches" for the natural history of gastropods) and possesses a muscular foot that acts like a powerful suction cup. By clamping its body against a rock, the limpet retains moisture under its shell during low tide and protects itself from predators.

Limpets attach to rocks using the force of vacuum suction. Attempting to remove a limpet from a rock or other hard surface, without damaging it, is exceedingly difficult. Once touched, the limpet spurts out a spray of water from its mantle, and creates an even greater vacuum between the surface and itself. If dislodged, the upside-down limpet has difficulty in turning itself over and becomes vulnerable to predators such as shore birds and sea stars.

Underneath the limpet's shell is a head with tentacles and a mouth, and a mantle containing its internal organs. Feathery gills are located just under the mantle covering. When submerged in water, the limpet holds its shell slightly off of the rock, allowing sea water to reach its gills. During low tide, the limpet continues to breath by retaining sea water and air between its shell and its body.

Vegetarian scrapes algae

The limpet is a vegetarian that uses its radula to scrape surface algae off rocks. It moves over the rock surface by secreting a slippery path of mucous which is produced by a special gland in the foot. Some species of limpets produce a mucous that encourages algae growth. The fertilizer-like mucous guarantees that there will be a continuous source of food.

Some species of limpets eat only when completely submerged with high tidal waters, while others prefer to forage only at night.

Homing behaviour

Many species of limpets display homing behaviour. These limpets have a specific resting spot that they always return to after their rounds of foraging for food. Many species prefer spots that are custom-made. By grinding on the rock with the margin of its shell, a homing scar becomes a perfect, watertight fit. These limpets then, not only return to the same spot, but always face in the same direction!

Broadcast fertilizer

The limpet has separate sexes and is a broadcast fertilizer. Like most other gastropods, the fertilized eggs develop into larvae which drift with the plankton before settling down on rocks along the shoreline.

Limpets, with a life span from five to sixteen years, often nestle together in groups or congregations in rock cracks and crevices along our shores.

Did you know that... as limpets and chitons scrape algae off rocks, they inadvertently scrape off newly settled larvae of many marine invertebrates, affecting the distribution and abundance of animals that live near them?

Tips for finding limpets

✪ Look on the shady side of boulders and inside rock crevices for limpets.

✪ Limpets can often be found living inside empty bivalve shells, along dock sides, and in small tidepools on a variety of beaches.

✪ Watch very closely for camouflaged limpets that have shells covered with tufts of algae.

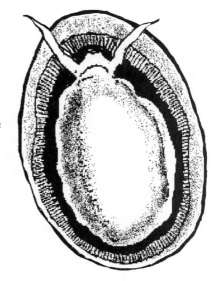

Looking Underneath a Limpet Shell

Tectura scutum

(=*Notoacmea scutum, Acmaea scutum*)
[Teck-TOUR-ah SKEW-tum]
Common name: Plate Limpet
Where: on rocky cliffs and boulders
Zone: middle to low intertidal
Colour: brown with white and dark spotting; occasionally green algae covers shell
Shape: oval and flattened, apex of shell not in centre and is rounded rather than pointed
Size: up to 6 cm (2.35 inches) long and 5 cm (2 inches) wide and 16 mm (.6 inches) high
Notes: Empty shells have inner white surface with a dark spot in the centre at apex and dark brown around the edges. Brown or dark coloured tentacles.

Tectura persona

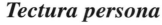

(=*Notoacmea persona, Acmaea persona*)
[Teck-TOUR-ah pair-SONE-ah]
Common names: Speckled Limpet or Mask Limpet
Where: always in the shade of rocks, in crevices or on lower edge of large boulders
Zone: high to middle intertidal
Colour: brownish grey, with white splotches on exterior; apex of shell is often encircled with grey and looks worn or eroded; occasionally dark spot in the interior apex
Shape: oval, almost rounded conical shape (looks over inflated), apex is slightly forward of centre of the shell and leans or inclines forward
Size: up to 5 cm (2 inches) long and 3.5 cm (1.4 inches) wide and 15 mm (.6 inches) high
Notes: Prefers the shade where freshwater seeps onto beach. Nocturnal feeder.

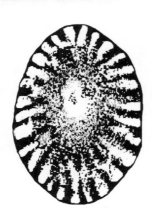

The Sea Star

Finding a sea star at the beach is a thrill for any seashore explorer. But why?

The sea star is not a rare animal; in fact, the British Columbia coastline has more species of sea stars than just about anywhere in the world. Perhaps its perfectly symmetrical, colourful body appeals to our sense of order and simplicity. Whatever it is, the sea star seems like an attractive, fascinating and pretty much harmless sea creature.

In reality, nothing could be further from the truth. Many species of sea stars are awesome predators with voracious appetites and amazing eating habits.

> ### Sea Star Facts
> **Species:** 2,000 world wide;
> 68 Pacific Northwest
> **Phylum:** Echinodermata, Class Asteroidea
> **Reproduction:** broadcast fertilization
> **Food:** variable depending on species, bivalves, plankton
> **Predators:** gulls, river otters
> **Life span:** 4 to 5 years, some species up to 20 years

All shapes and sizes

The sea star takes on all sorts of shapes and sizes. The arms emanate from a more or less flat central disk, the number of which varies according to the species.

Plates act like ribs

The rigidity of its body is created by calcareous plates or ossicles that act like ribs. Muscle and tissue fibre connected to the ossicles allow the body to bend. Some sea stars have exceedingly hard rigid bodies, while others have extremely soft or malleable ones.

The side of the sea star that is generally facing upwards, called the aboral side, appears to the naked eye to be featureless. But under a microscope, the entire surface of most species of sea stars is covered with tiny finger-like appendages and spines that serve a variety of functions.

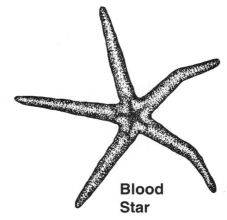

Blood Star

Sea star's gills

Short stalks called papulae or dermal branchiae are the sea star's gills. They jut out from holes in the sea star's hard calcareous plates and typically appear in clusters.

While other intertidal animals may have algae or barnacles attached to their bodies, the sea star has none. Most species have pedicellaria, long projections with pincers or scissor-like jaws at each tip, that surround the papulae. They open and snap shut when a foreign object touches them, thereby deterring any small organism or bits of sediment from covering the gills.

Swaying tube feet

On the sea star's oral side (or the side with the mouth), hundreds of swaying tube feet project from a gully or ambulacral furrow that runs the length of each arm.

These tube feet are moved by muscular contractions and can be retracted completely within the furrow for protection. Specialized tube feet at the end of each arm are used for touching as well as smelling. Minute reddish pigment spots at the end of the sea star's arms are light-sensitive organs.

The end of each tube foot of most local species of sea stars is shaped like a suction cup which it uses to attach to hard objects.

Internal water vascular system

The tube feet grip with vacuum suction, powered by a unique hydraulic system. Sea water is absorbed into an internal vascular canal system through the madreporite, a disk-shaped, porous plate that is clearly visible on the aboral side of the sea star.

A ring canal circles the mouth area while a major canal runs the length of each arm. The tube feet are connected to these canals via a globular-shaped bulb called an ampulla. When the ampulla is squeezed, water is forced down into the tube foot and the closed end balloons out or distends. It operates much like a common kitchen turkey baster does. When pressure on the ampulla is released, water is drawn back up into the bulb, and the tube foot is, in turn, contracted.

Microscopic Pedicellaria

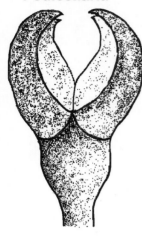

Did you know that...
pedicellaria and their arrangement are used by biologists to identify sea star species?

In order to get a grasping suction hold, the tube foot sits snugly against a hard object, and by withdrawing water pressure, a vacuum is formed. Trying to peel a sea star off the rocks is close to impossible. Usually the tube feet are torn off before the sea star releases its hold on the rocks.

Sea stars can grow a new arm

Fortunately for the sea star, its regenerative abilities are so impressive that losing a few tube feet is hardly a major setback.

If a sea star with an underdeveloped arm is found (see illustration of the Mottled Star, *Evasterias troschelli*), chances are it has lost it to a predator and is in the process of growing it back. Incredibly, as long as about one-fifth of the central disk and at least one arm are present, the sea star can completely regrow all missing body parts.

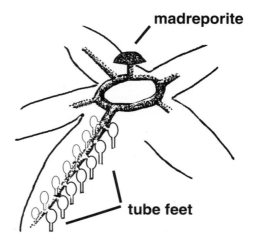

Sea Star's Water Vascular System

Sea stars can drop an arm

Some species of sea stars are capable of dropping or severing an arm in order to escape a predator. This process, called autotomization, occurs with the contraction of muscles against the sea star's calcareous plates.

Moving slowly or quickly

In order to move, the sea star pulls its body across hard surfaces by extending and then shortening its tube feet. Speed is determined, however, not by the number of arms or tube feet but by the rigidity of its body.

The Purple Star, *Pisaster ochraceus,* has a very rigid body and moves exceedingly slowly. The subtidal Sunflower Star, *Pycnopodia helianthoides*, however, is able to chase its prey at unbelievable speeds because its internal plates are not connected and the bendable body can move quickly with little muscular effort.

Some species are carnivores

Differences in eating behaviour vary from species to species. Many species of sea stars are voracious carnivores that eat barnacles, mussels, limpets and sea anemones.

The Purple Star, *Pisaster ochraceus*, for example, pries open a bivalve shell, such as a mussel, with its tube feet. The sea star extrudes its stomach up through its mouth and inserts it between the open gap between the shells. Digestive juices are secreted inside the mussel and the soft insides are slowly dissolved and absorbed. The sea star retracts its stomach back through its mouth and moves on to its next meal.

The Sunflower Star, *Pycnopodia helianthoides,* surrounds its prey and eats it "whole," spitting out any shell or unwanted bits after the soft parts have been digested.

Some species are plankton feeders

The local Blood Star, *Henricia leviuscula,* is a suspension feeder that catches plankton on its sticky mucous-covered surface. Cilia transports the food down line grooves that lead toward the sea star's mouth. Located in the centre of the disk on the oral side, a sea star's mouth moves by calcareous plates opening and closing.

Broadcast fertilizer

Most local sea stars are broadcast fertilizers. Sexes are separate, although it is impossible to determine the sex of a sea star from its external features. Eggs and sperm are shed directly into the sea water through tiny pores on the sea star's arms.

Larvae drift with the plankton before settling to the bottom. Some sea stars, like the Six-rayed Star, *Leptasterias hexactis,* and Blood Star, *Henricia leviuscula,* brood their eggs beneath their arched bodies. Amazingly, the female goes without eating for the entire brooding period, sometimes up to six weeks.

See also:

Pycnopodia helianthoides, Sunflower Star, in the chapter on "Floating Docks and Wharf Pilings."

Did you know that...
a number of species of sea stars migrate in groups from one feeding ground to another? During the winter, many sea stars migrate to deeper waters and return to shallower areas in the summer.

Evasterias troschelii

[Ev-ess-TEAR-ee-ass tross-KELL-ee]

Common name: Mottled Star or Troschel's Star

Where: on rocks, large boulders, on gravel beaches or sandy/mud bottoms

Zone: middle to low intertidal

Colour: extremely variable; blue/green to brown grey sometimes orangish (rarely pink or purple)

Shape: slender arms with medium disk

Texture: rigid, rough, sometimes mottled

Size: from 25 to 30 cm (10 to 12 inches) in radius

Notes: This drawing illustrates a sea star regenerating a new arm. Can be confused with Purple Star, *Pisaster ochraceus.*

Pisaster ochraceus

[Pie-ZASS-ter auk-RA-see-us]

Common names: Purple Sea Star, Ochre Sea Star

Where: on rocks, on large boulders, on gravel beaches, along mussel beds, on docks and pilings

Zone: middle to low intertidal

Colour: variable, salmon-pink to deep purple

Shape: large central disk, five plump tapering arms

Texture: very rigid with white hard spines or beads in a net-like pattern on its aboral surface

Size: up to 25 to 30 cm (10 to 12 inches) in radius

Notes: Most common intertidal sea star. Can live up to 20 years. Juveniles sometimes have six arms. Colour variability believed to be genetic.

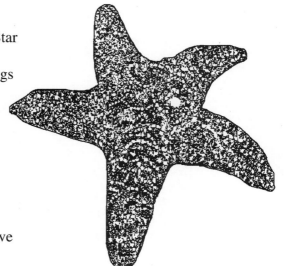

61

Henricia leviuscula

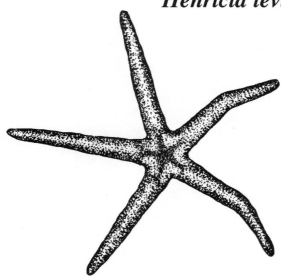

[Hen-REE-see-ah lee-view-SKEW-lah]
Common names: Blood Star or Pacific Henricia
Where: on rocks particularly near sponges and algae
Zone: low intertidal to subtidal
Colour: orange or orange red with disk often a different or mottled shade of red
Shape: thin arms and very small central disk
Texture: smooth
Size: from 10 to 18 cm (4 to 7 inches) in radius
Notes: Lacks pedicellaria. It is a ciliary plankton feeder; it traps organic particles on its mucous and moves them to its mouth. Smaller females brood their young in pouches around their mouths formed by their arched arms. Reported that larger females simply expel eggs into surrounding sea water.

Dermasterias imbricata

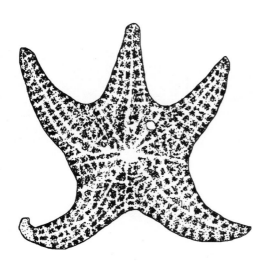

[Der-MASS-tear-ee-ass im-BREE-cat-ah]
Common name: Leather Star
Where: on rocky shores
Zone: low intertidal
Colour: reddish/brown with patches of greyish/purple; madreporite is bright yellow
Shape: large disk with five webbed arms
Texture: very smooth almost slimy
Size: from 20 to 25 cm (8 to 10 inches) in radius
Notes: Reportedly has a garlic or exploded gunpowder smell; will fight with members of its own species; eats sea cucumbers, sea anemones and sea urchins.

Leptasterias hexactis

[Lep-TASS-ter-ee-as hex-ACT-iss]
Common name: Six-rayed Star
Where: on rocks, big boulders on gravel shores
Zone: low intertidal to subtidal
Colour: variable, usually drab colours, grey/brown, olive green to purple/red
Shape: medium disk with six broad arms
Texture: stiff sometimes mottled surface
Size: up to 9 cm (3.5 inches) in radius
Notes: The only six-armed sea star in British Columbia, the female broods her eggs before they hatch. She holds them in a cluster with her tube feet and arches protectively over them.

Solaster stimpsoni

[Sew-LASS-ter stimp-SONE-ee]
Common name: Sun Star or Stimpson's Star
Where: sandy/muddy bottoms, rocks and gravel
Zone: low tide to subtidal
Colour: reddish/orange with greyish-blue band running down each arm
Shape: fairly large disk, 9 to 11 slender long arms
Size: from 23 cm to 50 cm (9 to 20 inches)
Notes: Eats sea cucumbers.

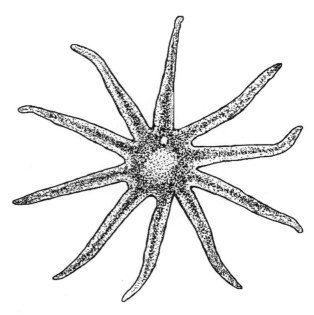

The Chiton

Near the low tide mark in the intertidal zone, the seashore explorer will find members of the Phylum Mollusca called the chiton, pronounced [KIE-ton].

Low Intertidal Zone dweller

The smaller species of chitons are not always obvious to find. The low profile of the chiton blends in so beautifully with its surroundings, who knows where rock ends and chiton begins?

Small species average from two to ten centimetres (.8 to 4 inches) in length and have drab black or brown-coloured shells. Their shells are practically flat and often covered with tufts of growing algae.

The chiton is primarily a nocturnal creature that has little tolerance for direct sunlight. When the tide is low during daylight hours, the chiton seeks refuge deep in damp rock crevices and under dark ledges, away from the seashore explorer's view.

Chiton Facts

Species: 600 world wide,
20 in Pacific Northwest
Phylum: Mollusca
Food: algae scraped off by a radula
Reproduction: broadcast fertilization
Predators: sea stars, crabs, fish

Bendable shell rolls up into ball

Sometimes called the sea cradle, the chiton has an eight-plated bendable shell. When removed from a rock, the chiton is capable of rolling up into a hard ball much like the common garden sow bug. This defensive behaviour protects the chiton from predators such as crabs, sea stars and shore birds.

Although the plates cover most of the chiton's body, around the outside edges, a thick and tough girdle grows that is, in some species, covered with bristles. The girdle not only holds the shells together but expands and contracts to assure waterproof contact against the rock surface, particularly during low tide.

Lacks tentacles

The chiton has a head that houses the mouth and salivary gland, and inside the fleshy mantle are its internal organs. The chiton, unlike the limpet, has no tentacles.

Between the mantle and the shells are feather-like gills that encircle the chiton. The number of gill fronds is dependent upon the species. Water is sucked or drawn in at the edges of the girdle, bathed around the gills and then expelled.

Nocturnal vegetarian

The chiton moves about by secreting a bed of mucous for its muscular foot to glide over. It feeds on algae by scraping the surfaces of rocks with its radula.

Many species of chitons go on nightly eating rounds, often following the same trail night after night and returning to the same spot by daybreak. Nervous structures called aesthetes found in small pits on the back of the chiton's plates sense light and darkness.

Broadcast fertilizer

Most species of chitons are broadcast fertilizers; males and females shed gametes into the surrounding sea water. In the larval stage, the chiton floats with the currents for many weeks until it settles onto a rock surface.

Tips for finding chitons

✪ Dead chitons with girdle and shells still intact can be commonly found along the shoreline. Some very attentive shore explorers find the butterfly-shaped plates in amongst bits of broken shell and stones.

✪ Look under rocks, in crevices, and under damp ledges away from direct sunlight.

✪ Sometimes chitons are active during daylight hours on foggy and cloudy days.

Did you know that...
the tiny teeth of a chiton's radula are composed of so much iron oxide (magnetite) that chitons can be picked up with a magnet?

Tonicella lineata

[Tawn-ee-SELL-ah linn-ee-AT-ah]
Common name: Lined Chiton
Where: on rocks, particularly those covered with coralline algae
Zone: middle to low intertidal to subtidal
Shape: oval to oblong; low profile, smooth and rounded
Texture/Pattern: smooth girdle, banded or striped shells
Colour: mottled reddish-brown to pink/lavender
Size: up to 5 cm (2 inches) long and 2.5 cm (1 inch) wide
Notes: Variable wavy lines of different colours on shells make this a very beautiful chiton.

Mopalia muscosa

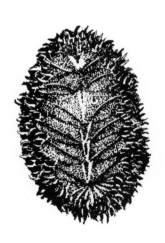

[Moe-PAL-ee-ah moose-COSE-ah]
Common name: Mossy Chiton
Where: on rocks and in tidepools
Zone: high to low intertidal but typically mid intertidal
Colour: dull brown, grey to green with lighter-coloured notch running down the middle
Shape: oval, flat
Texture: valves overgrown with algae; girdle is covered with stiff bristles
Size: up to 10 cm (4 inches) long and 5 cm (2 inches) wide
Notes: Tolerant of daylight and brackish water. Dead mossy chitons are often found washed up on rocky shores. The underside of the plates is blue.

The Sea Cucumber

The sea cucumber is an intriguing creature. It lives at the very low intertidal to the subtidal zones of rocky shores, usually under rocks or buried in sediment.

A full description of the natural history of the sea cucumber can be found in the chapter on "Sandy Beaches and Eelgrass Beds." Local species found under and in amongst the rocks are:

Parastichopus californicus

(=Stichopus californicus, Holthuria californica)

[Pair-a-stick-AH-pus kal-ee-FOR-knee-cuss]

Common name: Giant Red Cucumber or California Cucumber

Where: on rocky shores near mud/sand pockets, on docks and pilings

Zone: low intertidal to subtidal

Colour: dark red to purple with light-coloured spines

Shape: huge cucumber or long balloon shaped

Texture: sharp-looking spines on back that are really quite soft and harmless; tube feet on lower surface only

Size: up to 50 cm (19.6 inches) long and 12 cm (4.7 inches) wide

Notes: When approached by the predatory Sunflower Star, *Pycnopodia helianthoides,* the giant red cucumber rears its back up in self-defense. Juveniles are often found in crevices in vertical rock walls. Remains dormant in the winter months.

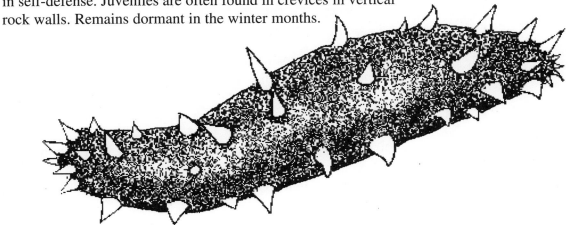

Eupentacta quinquesemita

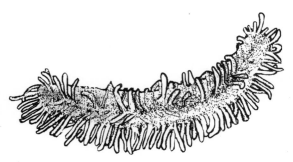

[You-pen-TACK-tah quin-kess-EE-me-tah]
Common name: White Cucumber or Stiff-footed Cucumber
Where: under rocks and in crevices
Zone: very low intertidal to subtidal
Colour: creamy/white to pale yellow
Shape: narrow with short bushy slimy tentacles surrounding mouth
Texture: five rows of stiff non-retractable tube feet around body
Size: up to 10 cm (4 inches) long and 4 cm (1.6 inches) wide
Notes: Very flaccid out of the water, its sac-like body slowly leaks sea-water from its tube feet and anus; attaches itself very tightly to rocks with its tube feet; can withdraw its tentacles completely inside its mouth. Eviscerates internal organs in autumn.

Cucumaria miniata

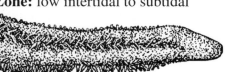

[Cue-koo-mar-EE-ah min-EE-at-ah]
Common name: Red or Orange Burrowing Cucumber
Where: in crevices and under rocks particularly in areas where the current is swift
Zone: low intertidal to subtidal

Colour: reddish/orange to brown body with darker-coloured tube feet and bright orange tentacles
Shape: cucumber-shaped body is typically curved in a crevice or under a rock so that only the tentacles are visible
Texture: smooth tough skin with ten highly branched tentacles surrounding mouth opening; 5 crowded rows of tube feet, two on upper side and three on bottom.
Size: 20 to 25 cm (7.8 to 10 inches) long and 4 to 5 cm (1.6 to 2 inches) wide when fully expanded
Note: Cannot tuck in its feeding tentacles inside its mouth.

The Sea Urchin

Deep down in the lowest regions of the intertidal zone, the seashore explorer may encounter the sea urchin, a relative of the sea star, sea cucumber and sand dollar (Phylum Echinodermata.)

Rounded wafer-thin plates

The urchin has a rounded shell made of wafer-thin plates, called a test. Covering the test are muscles and skin from which spines of various sizes and shapes are attached. By flexing the muscle, the urchin moves or rotates the spines. Some spines are long and sharp which burrow chambers into rocky cliffs. Other spines are shorter and equipped with pedicellaria or pinching jaws that protect the urchin's body from prey and foreign objects settling on it. Other spines behave like tube feet. Like sea stars, the urchin is able to regenerate missing body parts.

Complex eating apparatus

A complex five-pointed eating apparatus called Aristotle's lantern allows the sea urchin to scrape off encrusting algae or animals from rocks as the urchin moves about. Water is absorbed through the eating apparatus and is circulated throughout the body. Most species of urchins reproduce through broadcast fertilization.

Strongylocentrotus droebachiensis

[Strawn-gee-low-scent-TROW-tuss drow-back-EE-en-sis]
Common name: Green Sea Urchin
Where: rocky shores with some surf action and in tide pools
Zone: very low intertidal to subtidal
Colour: green with brown tinges, spines are usually paler colour and tube feet are purple
Shape: oval with short fine spines
Size: up to 8 cm (3.2 inches) wide and 3.5 cm (1.4 inches) high
Notes: An algae eater with a life span of four to eight years.

Did you know that...
the fully grown sea urchin has few enemies? The spines tend to discourage most predators, except for the occasional sea star, sea otter (on the outer coast) and human (in search of the urchin roe, a gastronomic delicacy in many parts of the world.)

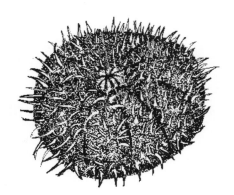

69

Fish

When overturning rocks and large boulders, don't be surprised to uncover a mass of squirming, writhing fish. These intertidal vertebrates can easily startle the unsuspecting seashore explorer.

Primarily subtidal dwellers

Although fish are primarily subtidal dwellers, many fish come into the intertidal region to either find food or lay eggs. Some have adapted to living between the tides, surviving the low water conditions by remaining hidden under rocks and between crevices until high water returns.

Well camouflaged in tidepools

Many of the smaller fish that live in tidepools have developed effective camouflage to hide from predators. Many lack swim bladders permitting the fish to remain at the bottom of the pool.

Egg clusters found under rocks

In the spring and early summer months, it is not uncommon to find fish under rocks guarding a cluster of eggs. The eggs are typically attached to the underside of the rock or boulder.

In some species, such as the Cockscomb Prickleback, *Anoplarchus purpurscens*, the female keeps the eggs oxygenated by continuously fanning them with her eel-like body.

The female of the Black Prickleback, *Epigeichthys atropurpureus*, lays the eggs under low intertidal rocks, but it is the male of the species that guards the eggs by encircling them with his body.

Six common species found intertidally

There are six common species of fish found intertidally. Look for most under large boulders or in tidepools, waiting for the return of high tidal waters. The diets of these fish species vary; however, small intertidal crustaceans form the bulk of their prey.

Oligocottus maculosus

[All-ee-go-CAUGHT-us mack-you-LOW-suss]
Common name: Tidepool Sculpin
Where: bottom dwellers of shallow waters, seen darting at the bottom of tidepools on rocky shores
Zone: high to middle intertidal
Colour: greenish to red above, belly blue or green tinted with white line below, fins are mottled or striped
Shape: stout, broad head tapers off to narrow end
Size: up to 9 cm (3.5 inches) long
Notes: Eyes are large and positioned high on the head. Tolerant of high temperatures and brackish water. Displays homing behaviour. If washed away by tidal currents, will return to original territory by its sense of smell.

Anoplarchus purpurescens

[Ann-oh-PLARK-us purr-purr-ESS-enns]
Common name: Cockscomb Prickleback, Crested Blenny
Where: under rocks on rocky sheltered shores
Zone: low intertidal
Colour: highly variable, grey/brown to olive body with lighter-coloured crest
Shape: eel-like with large fleshy crest on head and body
Size: up to 20 cm (7.8 inches) long
Notes: Most common eel-like fish found inter-tidally. The female lays eggs on undersides of rocks and keeps them oxygenated by fanning them with her body.

Epigeichthys atropurpureus

(=*Xiphister atropurpureus*)
[EH-pee-GICK-theese a-trow-purr-purr-EE-us]
Common name: Black Prickleback
Where: under rocks often near brackish water
Zone: low intertidal
Colour: brown to purple black with white stripe on base of tail
Shape: eel-like, with small head and pointed body with blunt tail
Size: to 30 cm (12 inches) long
Notes: The female lays eggs and the male guards them, encircling them with his body.

Porichthys notatus

(=*Porichthys myriaster*)
[Pour-ICK-theese no-TAT-us]
Common name: Plainfin Midshipman, Singing Fish
Where: under rocks and boulders in spring and summer
Zone: low intertidal
Colour: greenish-brown with black/blue on back, yellow belly
Shape: broad head with long body and protruding eyes
Size: up to 38 cm (15 inches) long
Notes: Female lays eggs under rocks and male guards them. Common name "Singing Fish" originates from the grunting sounds made by the bladder of the male. Notice rows of yellow spots that resemble brass buttons on a "midshipman's" uniform.

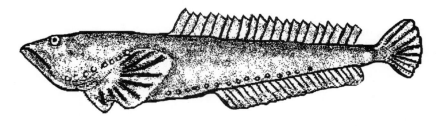

Gobiesox maeandricus

[GO-be-socks me-ANN-drick-us]
Common name: Northern Clingfish, Flathead
Clingfish
Where: clinging to the underside of smoothly
rounded rocks
Zone: middle to low intertidal
Colour: grey/brown with marbled dark and light
spots, light-coloured belly
Shape: very broad head and a narrow body
Size: up to 15 cm (6 inches) long
Notes: Pelvic fins on underside fused to form suction
cup for clinging upside-down to underside of rocks
and boulders. Will cling tightly to the palm of sea-
shore explorer's hand. Eats small crustaceans and
mollusks. Female deposits yellow eggs to undersides
of rocks and male guards the eggs.

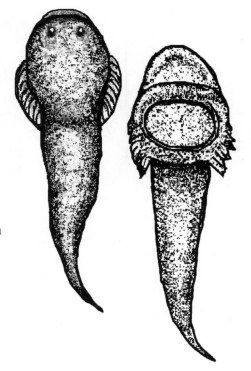

Apodichthys flavidus

[App-oh-DICK-theese fla-VEE-duss]
Common name: Penpoint Gunnel
Where: among eelgrass and seaweed
Zone: low intertidal
Colour: variable, bright green to shades of yellow and brown with
dark line or light spots running down side
Shape: eel-like fish with pointed anal fin
Size: up to 45 cm (18 inches)
Notes: Feeds primarily on small crustaceans. Green ones are un-
mistakeable.

Seaweed

Endocladia muricata

(=*Gigartina muricata*)

[Enn-doe-CLAD-ee-ah moor-ee-CAT-ah]
Common names: Sea Moss, Nailbrush
Phylum: Rhodophyta or Red Algae
Where: on rocks and hard surfaces
Zone: high intertidal
Colour: variable, pinkish red to black when dried out
Shape: cylindrical branches covered with short spines
Texture: dry, coarse, wire-like and very hard
Size: small, around 3 cm (1.2 inches) long
Notes: Bushy tufts often found underneath Rockweed, *Fucus sp.*
Sea moss is eaten by limpets.

Iridaea cordata

[Eye-rid-EE-ah core-DAT-ah]
Common name: Rainbow Seaweed
Phylum: Rhodophyta or Red Algae
Where: attached to rocks
Zone: low intertidal
Colour: dark bluish purple, iridescent in sunlight
Shape: broad thick blades form cluster attached to a disk-shaped holdfast. One blade tends to be larger than the others.
Texture: like sheets of rubber, thick with an almost oily-covered slickness
Size: blade typically 30 to 40 cm (12 to 15.75 inches) long
Notes: The colours of the rainbow are reflected on the blades by the sunlight, particularly spectacular when submerged in tidepool water. Very slippery to the touch.

Fucus sp.

[FEW-cuss]

Common name: Rockweed, Bladder Wrack
Phylum: Phaetophyta or Brown Algae
Where: attached to rocks and any hard surface
Zone: high intertidal
Colour: variable, mustard yellow to olive green
Shape: flattened fork-shaped stipes with two rounded points at each end, and a mid-rib running down the centre. Tips have swollen bladders. Holdfast is very small and disk-shaped with several stipes growing out of it.
Texture: spongy
Size: can grow up to 30 cm (12 inches) long; blades are about 1.5 cm (.5 inches) wide.
Notes: Use *Fucus sp.* as an indicator of where the lower boundary of the high intertidal zone begins. One of the most predominant algae in our intertidal region, found on any type of shoreline.

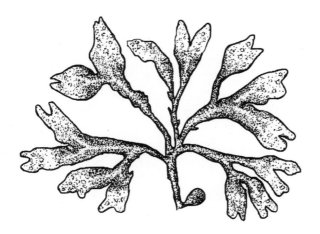

Rocky Shores and Tidepools Species Checklist:

☐	*Chthamalus dalli*	Little Acorn Barnacle
☐	*Balanus glandula*	Acorn Barnacle
☐	*Tectura scutum*	Plate Limpet
☐	*Tectura persona*	Speckled Limpet
☐	*Evasterias troschelii*	Mottled Sea Star
☐	*Pisaster ochraceus*	Purple Sea Star
☐	*Henricia leviuscula*	Blood Sea Star
☐	*Leptasterias hexactis*	Six-rayed Sea Star
☐	*Dermasterias imbricata*	Leather Sea Star
☐	*Solaster stimpsoni*	Sun Sea Star
☐	*Tonicella lineata*	Lined Chiton
☐	*Mopalia muscosa*	Mossy Chiton
☐	*Parastichopus californicus*	Giant Red Sea Cucumber
☐	*Eupentacta quinquesemita*	White Sea Cucumber
☐	*Cucumaria miniata*	Red Burrowing Sea Cucumber
☐	*Strongylocentrotus droebachiensis*	Green Sea Urchin
☐	*Oligocottus maculosus*	Tidepool Sculpin
☐	*Anoplarchus purpurescens*	Cockscomb Prickleback
☐	*Epigeichthys atropurpureus*	Black Prickleback
☐	*Porichthys notatus*	Plainfin Midshipman
☐	*Gobiesox maeandricus*	Northern Clingfish
☐	*Apodichthys flavidus*	Penpoint Gunnel
☐	*Endocladia muricata*	Sea Moss
☐	*Iridaea cordata*	Rainbow Seaweed
☐	*Fucus sp.*	Rockweed

SEASHORE EXPLORING LOG

Location: _____

_____

Date: _____

Shore Type: _____

Tide Level:

☐ High
☐ Mid
☐ Low

Plant and Animal Species

(observe the size and colour, where found in intertidal region, and what other animals/plants are close by)

Vancouver Island Shores I

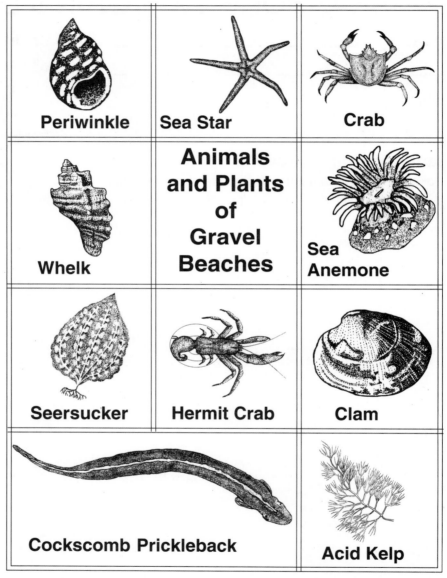

Periwinkle	**Sea Star**	**Crab**
Whelk	**Animals and Plants of Gravel Beaches**	**Sea Anemone**
Seersucker	**Hermit Crab**	**Clam**
Cockscomb Prickleback		**Acid Kelp**

Vancouver Island Shores I

GRAVEL AND COBBLESTONE BEACHES

Gravel and cobblestone beaches along the protected shores of the east coast of Vancouver Island are brimming with life. Often located under steep sea cliffs in the protection of rocky headlands, round, smooth cobblestones, usually 10 to 35 centimetres (4 to 14 inches) in diameter, carpet the intertidal landscape.

Walking along the cobblestone beach can be precarious. Smaller cobblestones tend to roll under the seashore explorer's feet, and balance is put to the test.

High tide beach is very narrow

At high tide, gravel and cobblestone beaches tend to be exceedingly narrow. The conifer forest grows down to the high tide mark. Hemlock and arbutus leaves are jumbled up with the cast-up fronds of colourful seaweed. Massive Douglas fir trees lean over the foreshore, providing shade for both the seashore explorer and the intertidal inhabitants below.

Mixed sediments at low tide

Due to the lack of strong wave activity or tidal currents, the cobblestone and gravel beach takes on quite a different character during low tide. Fine sediments like sand and mud are scattered in pockets among cobblestones and boulders below the high tide mark.

Overlap of creatures from rocky shores

The gravel, cobblestone, boulder, sand and mud provide a diverse habitat, and it is possible to find rock-dwelling, mud-dwelling, and sand-dwelling creatures scattered along the low-tide beach. In particular, there is considerable overlap of rocky intertidal inhabitants.

On Gravel Beaches, Look For

1
Periwinkle
2
Whelk
3
Shore Crab
4
Large Crab
5
Hermit Crab
6
Sea Anemone
7
Turkish Towel
8
Seersucker
9
Red Dulse
10
Sugar Wrack

Species and natural history of these creatures and plants are described in this chapter.

Large waves can carry away fine sediments

Occasionally, a beach that is sandy one year may be gravel and cobblestone the next year. Winter storms on the Strait of Georgia are usually to blame for altering the make-up of any shoreline. Larger than normal waves carry the sand and silt sediments from the shoreline into deeper waters, uncovering gravel and cobblestones.

Elliptical path of breaking waves

Water molecules move in an elliptical path when a wave breaks. On a sandy beach, the molecules penetrate the surface in amongst the tiny spaces between the sand particles and drain back out into deeper waters below the surface.

When winter storms bring larger and more frequent waves, the sand particles below the surface quickly become saturated and water molecules are forced to complete the elliptical journey above the surface. The water molecules carry fine particles of sand from the beach and deposit them in deeper waters in the strait.

Small waves create sandy shores

The same process cannot create sandy shores quite as quickly. The gentle, continuous lapping of waves onto a shoreline bring with them fine particles of sands from deeper water. Over time, the particles are deposited around large boulders on gravel and cobblestone beaches. Along protected shores, gentle waves create small sandy pocket beaches, so common along the east coast of Vancouver Island and in the Gulf Islands.

Parks with gravel and cobblestone beaches

Patricia Bay Park Saanich Peninsula
Kin Park Chemainus Duncan/Cowichan
Rathtrevor Provincial Park (north beach) Parksville
Kitty Coleman Beach Park Courtenay/Comox

More Animals To Look For On Gravel Beaches

Barnacle
Limpet
Sea Star
Fish
Clam
Oyster

Species and natural history of these creatures are described in other chapters.

The Periwinkle

Speckling the larger boulders and cobblestones on the gravel beach are small black spots that appear to be tiny pebbles or stones. These tiny specks are little snails known as periwinkles. Look around the tidepools amongst the boulders and gravel, and you will notice that the periwinkle lives on the edge of the tidepool, rather than immersed in it.

Living almost out of the water

Not at all keen about living in salt water, the periwinkle is sometimes called a littorine, which means "shore dweller" in Latin. The periwinkle prefers to live very high up on the shore in the spray zone and requires only an occasional moistening of sea water over its gills.

Some scientists believe that these snails are slowly evolving from sea creatures to land creatures. Many species of periwinkles can be kept out of sea water for six weeks or immersed in fresh water for as long as a week and a half without dire consequences.

Periwinkle Facts
Species: 175 world wide
Phylum: Mollusca, Class Gastropoda
Reproduction: eggs laid in gelatinous masses, some species have no planktonic dispersal
Food: eat algae on rock with radula
Predators: crabs, shore birds, fish

Operculum or trap door

The periwinkle's key to survival for long periods out of water is its operculum. This door-like structure near the entrance or aperture of its shell shuts so tightly it creates a watertight barrier between the animal's internal body and inclement weather, wind, fresh water and excessive heat of the outside world. It also protects the periwinkle from predators such as crabs, fish, shore birds and other snails.

Between the intermittent splashes of sea water in the spray zone, the periwinkle retains sea water inside its shell to continuously bathe its gills. As well, the periwinkle absorbs some oxygen from the air.

Periwinkle locomotion

The periwinkle, when emerged from its shell, looks very much like a common garden snail. It moves over a bed of slimy mucous that is secreted from a special gland in the foot. The muscular foot is separated in two by a groove, and the periwinkle waddles forward by moving one side of the foot, and then the other side.

Vegetarian with a radula

The periwinkle has a head with a mouth and two tentacles with light-sensitive cells located at the tips. The vegetarian periwinkle scrapes encrusted algae off rocks with its radula.

Sexual reproduction

Like other intertidal gastropods, the periwinkle never wanders very far from its birthplace in the intertidal zone. Periwinkles have separate sexes and males and females copulate. Eggs are fertilized within the female and then laid in gelatinous masses on rocks and boulders and under seaweed in the high intertidal zone.

Some species of periwinkles hatch out from the eggs in their adult form. There is never a free-drifting larval stage in its life cycle.

Tips for finding periwinkles

✪ Periwinkles are usually found higher up on the shore than barnacles. They are easily stepped on, particularly on sandstone shores, so take care where you walk.

✪ The periwinkle occurs on almost every type of shoreline. Check on rocks, boulders, under and on seaweed, as well as muddy/sandy shores.

✪ Look for tiny tracks left by the periwinkle as it slowly travels across mud flats.

Littorina scutulata

[Lit-or-EE-nah skew-two-LAT-ah]
Common name: Checkered Periwinkle
Where: rocks, boulders, in amongst seaweed
Zone: middle to high intertidal
Colour: brownish to almost black with white specks in a sort of checkerboard pattern, particularly near base and around spiral banding
Texture: smooth and shiny, thick shell
Shape: conical, rather slender, taller than it is wide
Size: to 1.5 cm (.6 inches) high and about 1 cm (.4 inches) wide
Notes: On rocks at low tide, look for this periwinkle in amongst the seaweed, under fronds and in around holdfasts.

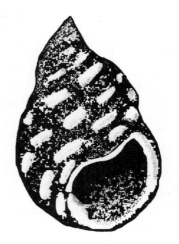

Littorina sitkana

[Lit-or-EE-nah sit-CAN-ah]
Common name: Sitka Periwinkle
Where: on rocks, boulders, in amongst seaweed and eelgrass
Zone: high intertidal
Colour: variable, dull grey or brown with light band near top of whorls
Texture: slight ridges
Shape: conically shaped, almost spherical
Size: 2 cm (.8 inches) high and 2 cm (.8 inches) wide
Notes: The aperture is very large compared to the size of the shell and almost perfectly round.

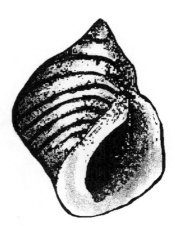

The Gastropod:
A Mollusk With One Shell or Valve

**Nudibranch:
the shell-less
gastropod**

Gastropods are an extremely diverse group in appearance, habits and habitat. Sometimes referred to as univalves, meaning one valve, the gastropod is a member of the Phylum Mollusca.

Gastropods include periwinkles, moon snails, limpets, whelks, and even the shell-less marine sea slugs called nudibranchs.

The gastropod has a head with tentacles, and a large fleshy, mucous-coated foot which it uses to move.

The gastropod's shell can be flattened or tent-shaped, or conical or spiral as in an elongated cone wound around an axis.

On a spiral shell, each turn around the axis is a whorl. The body whorl which contains most of the body parts is the largest and most recently formed. The remaining whorls constitute the spire which terminates at the apex. The apex is actually the original shell from the gastropod's larval stage.

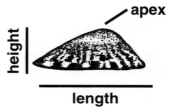

Did you know that...
the size of a flattened or tent-shaped shell is described in terms of length, measured from the front to rear of the shell?

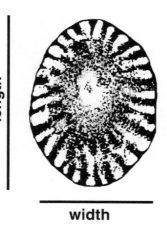

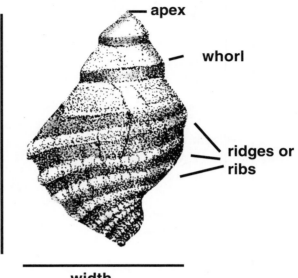

apex

whorl

ridges or ribs

height

width

Did you know that...
when measuring a spiral-shelled gastropod, the term height indicates the distance from the top or apex to the end of the shell near the aperture?

Many spiral-shelled gastropods have a shell-like lid called an operculum attached to the side of the fleshy foot. This is used like a door that neatly seals off the opening or aperture of the shell from external elements and predators.

Annual growth rings or ridges are visible on gastropod shells, particularly larger spiral shells like those of the moon snail.

Gastropods can be vegetarian, carnivorous or omnivorous. Inside the mouth is a radula, a ribbon of tiny teeth that works much like a food grater.

Herbivorous gastropods use their radula to scrape surface layers of algae off of rocks or other hard surfaces. Carnivorous gastropods drill into the shells of mollusks with their radula. An acidlike or chemical mucous is secreted to assist in the erosion of the shell.

A well-developed sense of smell aids the gastropod in defending itself against its enemies. If a gastropod senses an approaching predator or detects the scent of a wounded gastropod of the same species, it quickly moves away and seeks refuge.

Moon Snail: Largest Gastropod Along Our Shores

The Whelk

The common names "Dogwinkle" or "Dog Whelk" are often used to describe this seashore snail, but the canine reference comes from the old English word that means "small" rather than any reference to the four-legged animal.

Round variable shells

The spiral shell of the whelk is cylindrical or tubular, a design that seems to protect the long siphon the animal uses to draw in water to bathe its gills. Variability in shell textures and colours make the various whelk species difficult to identify.

Whelk Facts
Phylum: Mollusca, Class Gastropoda
Food: eats mussels and barnacles with its radula
Reproduction: by copulation, eggs laid in capsule clusters
Notes: nocturnal and diurnal scavenger
Life span: up to 10 years

The variety of shell colours, even within the same species, is believed to reflect the culinary habits of the whelk. White-coloured shells result from a diet rich in barnacles, while brownish-grey shells result from a mostly mussel diet.

Scavengers of the intertidal region

Whelks are known as scavengers, well prepared to clean up a dead fish or bivalve that may float ashore. In order to get at the meat of a shell-covered crustacean or mollusk, the whelk uses its tonguelike proboscis which is equipped with a rasping radula at the end.

Look closely at a bed of barnacles, and you may find a whelk in the process of eating. It either batters at the barnacle's operculum plates until it pries them apart or slowly drills through the shell with its radula.

Through the narrow round hole it produces, the whelk extends its proboscis and scrapes out its victim's flesh. It is a slow process. Studies indicate it can take up to two days for a whelk to drill and eat a barnacle.

Eggs layed in clusters

Sexes are separate in most whelks and copulation does occur. The female lays hundreds of egg capsules in clusters amongst the boulders and rocks, but not all develop. Amazingly, many of the eggs laid by the whelk are sterile and are eaten by the larvae that do hatch.

Life span varies from species to species, but whelks have been known to live up to ten years.

See also:

In the chapter on "Mud Flats," see also the following whelks:
Ocenebra japonica, the Japanese Oyster Drill,
Ilyannassa obsoletus, the Black Dog Whelk,
Batillaria cumingi, the Screw Shell.

Nucella emarginata

(=Thais emarginata)
[New-SELL-ah ee-marj-in-AT-ah]
Common names: Ribbed Dogwinkle or Striped Dogwinkle
Where: on rocks and docks near mussel beds
Zone: mid to low intertidal
Colour: variable, greyish/black to brownish/yellow with white on ribs
Shape: spire conical with thick plump shell
Size: to 3 cm (1.2 inches) high and 2 cm (.8 inches) wide
Texture: variable, usually ribs of varying thickness
Notes: Interior of shell is purple. Used as home for small hermit crabs.

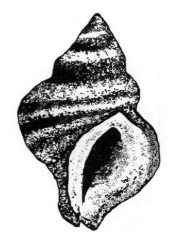

Nucella lamellosa

(=Thais lamellosa)
[New-SELL-ah lamb-ell-OH-sa]
Common names: Wrinkled Purple Whelk, Frilled Dogwinkle
Where: on rocks, among barnacles and mussels
Zone: high to middle intertidal
Colour: pale brown or grey
Shape: spire conical with seven convex whorls, can be quite frilly or ornamental
Size: up to 5 cm (2 inches) high and 2 cm (.8 inches) wide
Prey: barnacles, clams, mussels, oysters
Texture: typically heavily ridged or fluted, although this depends on exposure to waves
Notes: In spring and summer, look for the large clusters of its yellow egg cases on the underside of moist rocks.

Lirabuccinum dirum

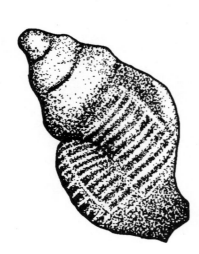

(=Searlesia dira)
[Lye-rah-bux-SIN-um DEAR-um]
Common names: Dire Whelk or Spindle Whelk
Where: rocky shores, large rocks on gravel beaches
Zone: middle intertidal
Colour: very dull grey shell, body mantle is white
Shape: spire conical with five or six whorls and evenly spaced ribs
Texture: raised
Size: to 5 cm (2 inches) high and 2 cm (.8 inches) wide
Note: Preys on barnacles, worms and injured sea creatures.

The Crab

Washed ashore on every type of beach, and scattered among the debris of seaweed and empty shells, are pieces of crabs: a leg or part of the carapace. Occasionally, a complete body with all limbs attached is found. Many novice seashore explorers incorrectly believe that the crab is dead but in all likelihood, it is a discarded outgrown or moulted exoskeleton.

Dead or moulted crab?

To determine whether a moulted exoskeleton or a dead crab has been found, smell it. If it has a strong odour, it is probably dead. If not, check out the back, upper edge of the crab's shell. If it opens much like the lid on a garbage can, a moult has been found.

> ### Crab Facts
> **Phylum:** Arthropoda
> **Reproduction:** sexes copulate, female carries fertilized eggs under tail
> **Food:** scavengers, herbivores and carnivores depending upon species
> **Predators:** shore birds, other crabs
> **Life span:** small shore crabs live 2 to 3 years, larger crabs can live up to 8 years of age.

Growth by moulting

All crabs, no matter what size, grow by moulting their chitinous exoskeleton or cuticle.

When the crab's shell begins to feel a little too snug, hormones stimulate the production of a new soft shell under the old. Enzymes dissolve the inside of the old cuticle, and by absorbing sea water and swelling the body, a fault-line or crack develops at the hind edge of the old carapace.

By expelling fluid, the crab shrinks small enough to be able to climb out of its outgrown shell. The crab backs out through the crack in the carapace, carefully pulling out its limbs, feelers and mouth parts.

After moulting, the crab finds itself in a too-tight soft shell. By absorbing sea water, the new shell expands to a more comfortable fit and affords room for new growth.

Moulting frequency varies with age

The crab's new shell hardens in about forty-eight hours with the intake of calcium carbonate which the crab extracts from the sea water. Occasionally a crab is seen eating its old shell which is an excellent calcium carbonate source.

A crab increases in size from moult to moult anywhere from eleven to thirty percent of its previous body size. Young crabs may moult once every two weeks, but mature crabs, depending on the amount of food eaten and life expectancy, moult once a year or less. Moulting and mating are inextricably entwined in the life of the crab. If a crab did not moult, copulation between the male and female could not occur.

Crab reproduction

The male crab deposits sperm from its gonopod into a special abdominal receptacle near the female's two central walking legs that is accessible only when her shell is soft. In a precopulatory courtship, the male grasps onto the female and carries her around, sometimes for days, until she moults.

After successful copulation, the male continues to hold onto the female until her new carapace has hardened. By doing so, he protects her from potential predators.

Most mating occurs in the summer months, while the actual fertilization of eggs typically occurs later in the fall.

Eggs attached under female's tail

The fertilized eggs are extruded from inside the female's body and become attached to the small appendages under her tail by a fast-hardening mucous. A female crab is referred to as "berried" when carrying her eggs, and often she is so ripe with eggs that her tail is forced up and away from her body. Depending upon the species, female crabs can produce up to a million eggs annually. A transparent swimming larva emerges from the egg and floats in amongst the sea water. As it moults, it transforms into a crab-like megalops stage and loses its ability to swim. After many moults, an adult crab is formed.

Did you know that... male crabs and female crabs are easy to distinguish? The triangular-shaped tail of the female is typically broader and more U-shaped than the male's narrower and V-shaped tail.

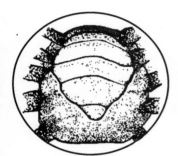

Female Crab

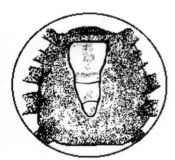

Male Crab

Pincers and self defense

For self defense, the crab's pincers are a fairly convincing deterrent for any predator. Pincers are able to cut through human flesh quite handily, and the large pincers of the Dungeness Crab, *Cancer magister,* can break human bones.

If the pincers are not enough to discourage a potential predator, the crab can always forfeit a limb and regenerate a new one over the next few moults. By spasmodically contracting the muscles at a fracture line along the leg, the crab releases the limb with minimal bleeding since few muscles or nerves pass through this joint. The entire process is called autotomization; a special muscle closes the wound, and the crab's colourless blood coagulates quickly.

Crab is a scavenger

The crab uses its pincers for more than just defensive purposes. Pincers are its eating utensils used for grasping and tearing its food.

Primarily scavengers, many species of crabs eat the flesh of dead animals. Along with its pincers, the crab has an assortment of mouth appendages that sort, cut and pulverise its food. It must process its food before ingesting it because the crab has a fairly small gullet that can handle only finely chopped food. Appendages push food into its mouth and stomach teeth continue the food grinding process. The crab excretes unused wastes through an anal opening at the rear of the carapace.

Small paddle-like appendages near the mouth fan the sea-water into the mouth and over the crab's well-developed set of gills. The gills are attached to the base of each leg and when the crab is uncovered during low tide, internal sea-water is retained to bathe the gills.

A crab's senses

The visual, chemical and tactile senses of the crab are well developed. It possesses a nervous system that controls antennae and sensory hairs for touch, and compound eyes for seeing.

Did you know that...
the crab does not swim? It runs on the pointed tips of its legs and always in a sideways direction. The legs on one side of the body pull while those on the opposite side push. The ability to run fast sideways may be a defensive behaviour, aimed at confusing predators such as fish and shore birds by taking a sideways escape route.

Crab In One Of Its Microsopic Larval Stages

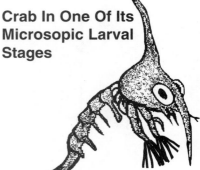

91

Petrolisthes eriomerus

[Pet-row-LISS-theese err-ee-oh-MARE-us]
Common name: Porcelain Crab
Where: in amongst rocks and gravel and in mussel beds
Zone: high to low intertidal, very common
Colour: variable, brownish-green to reddish-brown
Shape: oval carapace appears granular and flattened, extremely large, long pincers relative to body size; only 4 pairs of legs
Size: to 2 cm (.75 inch) wide by 2.5 cm (1 inch) long
Notes: Large claws very easily autotomotized or dropped to escape predators; filter-feeds by fanning plankton and detritus into mouth.

Hemigrapsus oregonensis

[Hem-ee-GRAP-us oar-ee-GONE-en-sis]
Common names: Green or Yellow Shore Crab
Where: near brackish water on rocky, gravel or muddy beaches
Zone: mid to low intertidal
Colour: variable, upper surface yellowish-green to olive-grey, pincer tips are white
Shape: smooth rounded carapace with hairy legs
Size: to 3.5 cm (1.2 inches) wide by 3 cm (1.25 inches) long
Notes: Has permanent burrows in mud that it escapes into to avoid predators.

Hemigrapsus nudus

[Hem-ee-GRAP-us NUDE-us]
Common names: Purple Shore Crab
Where: under most loose rocks on rocky
and gravel beaches
Zone: high to low intertidal
Colour: variable within species, but predominantly purple with white patterns on
upper surface, white underneath, purple
spots on pincers
Shape: smooth rounded carapace with no
visible leg hairs
Size: to 5 cm (2 inches) wide by 5 cm
(2 inches) long
Notes: Eats algae on rocks as well as dead
animal matter.

Pugettia gracilis

[Pew-JET-ee-ah grass-ILL-iss]
Common name: Graceful Spider Crab,
Graceful Kelp Crab
Where: among eelgrass beds and sea-
weed on all shores
Zone: low intertidal
Colour: variable, usually brownish green
Shape: shield shaped with short spines
Size: to 5 cm (2 inches) wide by 5 cm
(2 inches) long
Notes: Occasionally the rostrum or
pointed edges of the carapace near its
eyes and mouth are camouflaged with
bits of algae.

Cancer productus

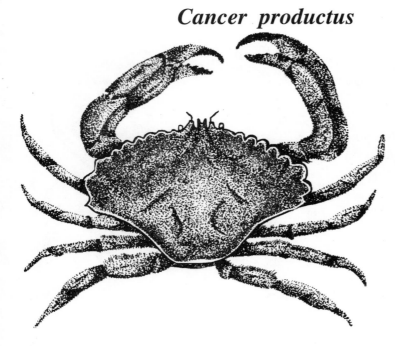

[CAN-sir
pro-DUCT-us]
Common name: Red Rock
Crab
Where: among rocks, near
large boulders on gravel shores
Zone: low intertidal
Colour: brownish-red carapace
underside yellowish-white,
black-tipped pincers
Shape: fan-shaped with ser-
rated edge
Size: up to 18 cm (7 inches)
wide by 10 cm (4 inches) long

Cancer magister

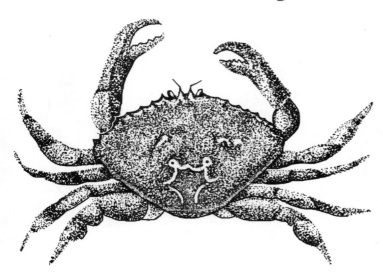

[CAN-sir MAJ-iss-ter]
Common names: Pacific,
Commercial, Edible or
Dungeness Crab
Where: buried in sandy or
muddy substrates and among
seaweed and eelgrass
Zone: low intertidal to
subtidal
Colour: mottled purple on
surface with cream colour
underneath
Shape: fan-shaped with
serrated edge
Size: 23 cm (9 inches) wide by
16 cm (6.3 inches) long
Notes: Eats worms, clams. Life
span 6 to 8 years.

Pugettia producta

[Pew-JET-ee-ah pro-DUCT-ah]
Common name: Northern Kelp Crab
Where: rocks, on brown algae
Zone: low intertidal
Colour: olive green to reddish brown with dark spots on upper surface, pale underneath
Shape: smooth, shield-shaped
Size: 9 cm (3.5 inches) wide by 12 cm (4.8 inches) long
Notes: Dislikes brackish water. Eats algae in summer, barnacles and hydroids in winter.

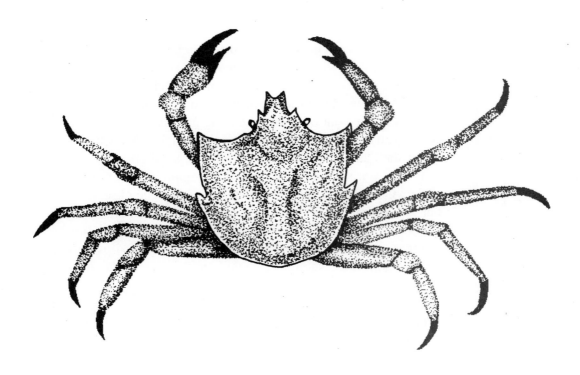

The Hermit Crab

Closely related to ghost shrimp, watch for the tiny hermit crab in tidepools along gravel and rocky shores. In order to protect its soft hind end (it lacks a hard exoskeleton), the hermit crab tucks it inside an empty spiral shell. Using its last pair of legs like hooks, the hermit crab fastens to the inside of a shell and scuttles about carrying its home on its back. Its pincers and antennae extend beyond the shell's aperture opening, but when threatened by a predator, the hermit crab retreats completely inside the shell, using its pincers to close the end of the shell much like an operculum.

> **Hermit Crab Facts**
> **Species:** 28 in Pacific Northwest
> **Phylum:** Arthropoda
> **Reproduction:** male and female emerge halfway out of their shells to copulate
> **Food:** detritus, omnivorous scavenger

Intertidal juggler

The hermit crab must continually search for a larger shell to accomodate its growing body. When an empty shell is found, it turns it over and over, as though the crab were closely inspecting it from every angle. If the shell is deemed large enough, the hermit crab quickly slips out of its old shell and into the new one to see how it fits. If it is not satisfactory, it quickly changes back to the original shell and continues to hunt for a larger shell.

Empty spiral shells in the intertidal region are a limiting resource. Occasionally aggressive behaviour can be observed. When two hermit crabs of varying sizes meet, the smaller crab of the two will surrender its shell to the larger crab. If the shell suits the bigger crab, it scuttles away and the smaller crab slips into the forfeited shell. If the shell isn't suitable to the larger crab, the crabs each revert back to their original shells.

The hermit crab is primarily a scavenger. It has similar eating appendages and behaviours as other crabs, and must pulverize its food before ingestion.

Mating behaviour is also similar to other crabs. Both male and female emerge about halfway out of their shells in order to copulate. The female typically broods her eggs inside her shell rather than under her tail.

Pagurus granosimanus

[Pag-ER-us gran-oss-ee-MAN-us]
Common name: Granular Hermit Crab
Where: rocky and gravel/cobblestone shores
Zone: high to middle intertidal
Shell: smaller crabs use periwinkle shells; larger crabs use whelk shells
Colour: greenish-brown carapace with bluish-spotted pincers and legs, red antennae
Shape: pear-shaped, hairless
Size: to 2 cm (.8 inches)
Notes: Look in tidal pools on rocky shores and in pools of water on gravel shores. Watch for the fairly quick movement of a periwinkle or whelk shell across the bottom. The antennae and claw will be peeking out of the shell opening or aperture.

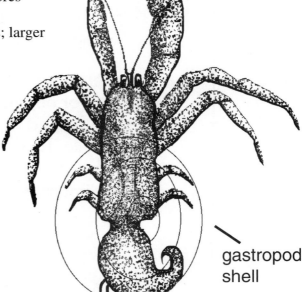

gastropod shell

Pagurus hirsutiusculus

[Pag-ER-us her-suit-tea-is-SKEW-luss]
Common name: Hairy Hermit Crab
Where: rocky and gravel/cobblestone shores
Zone: high to middle intertidal
Shell: smaller crabs use periwinkle shells, larger crabs use whelk shells
Colour: orangish-brown; light/dark bands on two green antennae
Shape: pear-shaped with very hairy greenish-brown legs
Size: to 2.5 cm (1 inch)
Note: Often seen in shell which is too small for the crab.

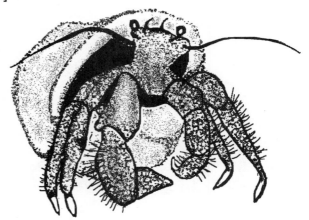

The Pea Crab

Shellfish harvesters are often surprised to find a tiny crab living inside the shell of a clam or other bivalve mollusk.

Living inside a clam

The commensal pea crab sustains itself inside the bivalve by eating microscopic plankton that is collected on mucous inside the mollusk and in the water circulating inside the shell.

Parasitic or commensal

Although the pea crab does not eat the flesh of the bivalve, it may damage the clam's mantle and gills and could be considered a parasite.

Sexual dimorphism

Female and male pea crabs differ enormously in size, so much so that the two crabs were first thought to be of different species. The adult female pea crab is typically much larger than the male and grows so large that she is unable to leave the confines of the bivalve's shells.

In the early stages of their adult lives, when this incongruity in size is not as severe, the pea crabs exit from their respective bivalve shells and mate externally. When the female becomes too large to exit the shell, the male must enter the host shell where mating occurs.

Pinnixa subquadrata

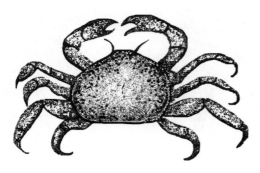

[Pin-ICKS-ah sub-quad-RAT-ah]
Common name: Pea Crab
Where: inside clams such as the Horse Clam, *Tresus capax*
Colour: brownish yellow
Shape: round and somewhat oblong carapace
Size: about 1.5 cm (.6 inches) long

The Sea Anemone

Is it an animal or is it a plant? Studied since Aristotle's time (384 - 322 BC), the sea anemone's flower-like appearance confused most scientists until the 1800s when it was discovered that the sea anemone was an animal from the Phylum Cnidaria [nigh-dare-EE-ah], a relative of the jellyfish.

The creature is not complex. It has a stalk which contains a hollow gut, a mouth, located at the centre top of the stalk which opens and closes like a drawstring purse, and tentacles surrounding the mouth. The base of the stalk, called the pedal disk, attaches by vacuum suction to solid objects such as rocks, docks and even the fronds of certain seaweeds.

Capable of changing its shape

The sea anemone's body is amazingly elastic. Many species have the ability to alter their appearance. The anemone withdraws its tentacles inside its mouth and contracts its gelatinous body.

Stinging cells capture food

Most sea anemones are carnivores that capture prey on tentacles that are equipped with millions of microscopic stinging cells called cnidocytes [nigh-DOE-sights]. Each contains a nematocyst [knee-MAT-toe-sist] which discharges a sticky substance or a potent toxin that, upon contact, stuns its prey. The victim is then transferred from the anemone's tentacles to its mouth.

Plumose Sea Anemone

Defensively, the nematocysts are used to sting potential predators such as sea stars and fish. Local species do not have stinging cells potent enough to hurt humans.

Nematocysts are discussed in more detail in the chapter on "Floating Docks."

Asexual and sexual reproduction

Many species of sea anemones have separate sexes and reproduce by releasing gametes from the gut via the mouth to the surrounding sea water. Other species are hermaphrodites that are capable of either sexual or asexual reproduction.

Did you know that...
the green colour of many sea anemones is really the colour of millions of symbiotic algae that live within the anemone's tentacles and gastrovascular cavity?

In some species, the sea anemone asexually reproduces by developing polyps at its pedal disk base which grow into miniature sea anemones. In other species, offspring develop from a small piece of body tissue that is torn away from the parent's body when the pedal disk is expanded then quickly withdrawn.

The ability to reproduce both sexually and asexually has many advantages. If an anemone has found an ideal habitat with room for expansion, it can reproduce asexually, creating a massive genetically identical colony.

War between two genetically identical colonies

Occasionally, cloning wars between two genetically different groups of anemones occur. When the two separate colonies spread out over one rock surface, for example, the anemones at the edge of each colony eventually touch. The battle begins when the opposing anemones produce enough toxins from their tentacles that each is rendered sterile. As a result, asexual expansion of either anemone colony is no longer possible and the colonies begin to reproduce by broadcast fertilization. Gametes are shed into the surrounding water and the larvae are transported by the currents up the shoreline to establish new territories and colonies.

Since sea anemones are able to clone themselves, determining the age of a particular animal is difficult. However, in the laboratory setting, some sea anemones have lived for 80 years, and many scientists believe that, in the wild, some species can live between 100 to 200 years.

Sea anemone movement

While movement is not of great importance to the mostly sessile sea anemone, it is possible for the anemone to move very slowly by muscular contraction of its pedal disk.

Tips for finding sea anemones

✪ Look for sea anemones on almost all types of beaches along the east coast. On sandy shores, sea anemones are attached to a rock or shell located under the surface sands.

✪ Because the sea anemone is very capable of altering the shape of its body, it can look very different during low tide. With its tentacles retracted, it may appear to be a round gelatinous blob. As well, to conserve moisture during low tide, some species of sea anemone pulls in its tentacles and camouflages itself with small pieces of shell and pebbles which attach to rough spots called tubercles along its body stalk.

✪ By gently touching the end of the anemone's tentacles, you may be able to feel the "sticky" nematocysts.

See also:

Metridium senile, Plumose Sea Anemone, in chapter on "Floating Docks and Wharf Pilings."
Epiactis prolifera, Brooding Sea Anemone, in chapter on "Sandy Beaches and Eelgrass Beds."

Tealia crassicornis

(=Tealia felina, Urticina crassicornis)
[Tea-LEE-ah crass-ee-CORN-iss]
Common name: Northern Red Anemone
Where: attached to rocks on shady side or under seaweed
Zone: low intertidal to subtidal
Colour: red, often mottled shades of red with very dull green splotches
Size: up to 8 cm (3 inches) wide and 8 cm (3 inches) high
Shape: smooth column with thick blunt tentacles
Notes: Larger specimens are found in the subtidal region.

Anthopleura elegantissima

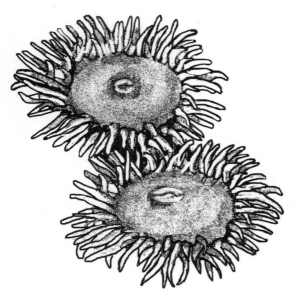

[Ann-thow-PLUR-ah
el-ee-gant-TEASE-ee-ma]
Common names: Aggregating, Rough or
Pink-tipped Anemone
Where: on rocks often in large colonies or
large clusters
Zone: middle to low intertidal zone
Colour: olive-green tentacles with pinkish
purple tips. Tentacles and central oral disk
are the same colour as the column.
Shape: round oral disk with tentacles
Size: basal disk up to 5 cm (2 inches) wide
to 8 cm (3 inches) wide when tentacles are
open and 2.5 cm (1 inch) high
Notes: At low tide, folds in tentacles. Colonies are usually clonal groups although both
sexual and asexual reproduction is possible.
Green colour in tentacles is from symbiotic
algae.

Anthopleura artemisia

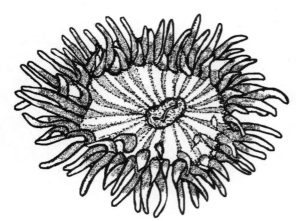

[Ann-thow-PLUR-ah art-em-EE-see-ah]
Common names: Moonglow, Green Burrowing, Buried Sea Anemone
Where: attaches itself to rocks or shells
under sandy/muddy surfaces
Zone: low intertidal to subtidal zone
Colour: variable greenish tentacles often
banded with white, pink tips; oral disk is
pinkish; upper part of stalk is greyish
Size: up to 7 cm (2.75 inches) wide and 3 cm
(1.25 inches) high
Notes: Column has tubercles which are
covered with bits of sand and shell. May
completely contract itself below the surface
during low tide.

Seaweed

On gravel and cobblestone beaches, a variety of the most common seaweeds, such as Rockweed, *Fucus sp.*, and Sea Lettuce, *Ulva sp.*, can be found.

Coarse gravel beaches in sheltered bays close to headlands are great places to search for subtidal seaweeds that have been cast ashore. Often there are several distinct lines of dried and drying seaweed along the upper part of the gravel and cobblestone beach.

Each line of seaweed indicates the last level of tidal water. If there is only one line of seaweed, that line represents the last high tide and also indicates that the tide was higher than the preceding one. If there is more than one line of seaweed, the lower line indicates the height of the last high tide and also that the last tide did not reach as far up the beaches as the previous tide.

Porphyra perforata

[Pour-FIE-rah purr-for-AT-ah]

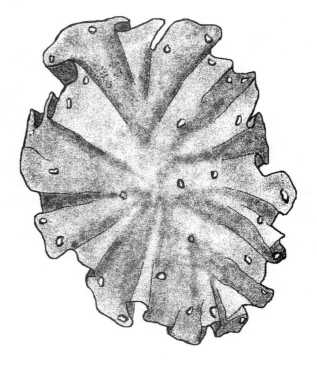

Common names: Red Dulse, Purple or Red Laver
Phylum: Rhodophyta or Red Algae
Where: grows in low intertidal zone, often on larger boulders on gravel beaches
Colour: variable but predominantly brownish purple and iridescent
Shape: large thick blades with ruffled ends, tiny perforations near the edges of the blades
Texture: rubber-like, similar in texture to Rainbow Seaweed, *Iridaea cordata.*
Size: 30 to 50 cm long (12 to 20 inches) long, blade to 30 cm (12 inches) wide
Notes: There are numerous species of *Porphyra* and identification may be difficult for the novice seashore explorer.

Mastocarpus papillatus

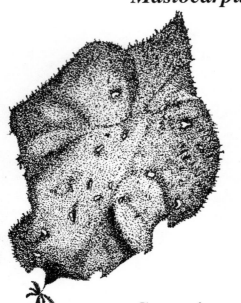

[Mass-toe-CAR-puss pap-ill-AT-us]
Common name: Turkish Towel or Washcloth
Phylum: Rhodophyta or Red Algae
Where: low tidal zone to subtidal, but frequently washed up on gravel shores
Colour: purplish brick red to almost black/red
Shape: broad oval-shaped thick blades. Can have more than one blade growing from disk-shaped holdfast
Texture: bristly growths all over blade, resembles the coarse bristles on a cotton towel, hence common name
Size: 30 to 40 cm (12 to 16 inches) long.

Costaria costata

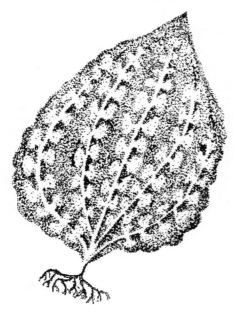

[Koss-tar-EE-ah koss-TAT-ah]
Common name: Seersucker
Phylum: Phaetophyta or Brown Algae
Where: found in the low intertidal to subtidal, often found cast up on shore on gravel beaches
Colour: brown
Shape: single long broad blade growing from disk-shaped holdfast
Texture: Six rows of raised or puckered ribs run up and down the long blade looking like seersucker material hence the common name. The puckers are prominent on only one side of the blade.
Size: variable, typically around 10 to 30 cm (4 to 12 inches) long but up to 1 metre (3 feet) in length can be found.

Laminaria saccharina

[Lam-ee-NAR-ee-ah sack-are-EE-nah]
Common names: Sugar Kelp or Sugar Wrack
Phylum: Phaetophyta or Brown Algae
Where: attaches to rocks or other large algae in low tide zone
Colour: olive or rich yellow-green to brown
Shape: long oval-shaped blade with two rows of ripple marks up and down its length from a stipe that is around 10 cm (4 inches) long. Holdfast almost rootlike in appearance
Texture: smooth and rubbery, sometimes torn longitudinally down blade
Size: 1 to 2 metres (3 to 6.5 feet) long and 18 cm (7 inches) wide
Notes: An edible seaweed that contains Vitamin C and sugars. Susceptible to pollutants. Older plants may have other algae and small animals growing on them.

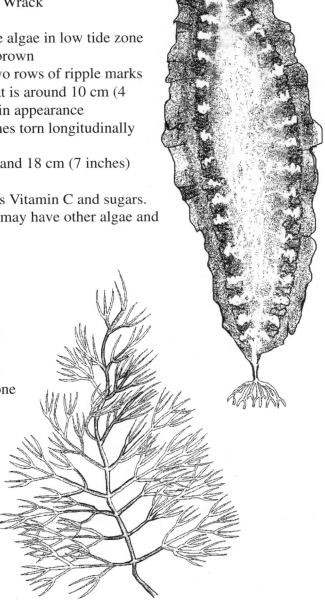

Desmarestia viridis

[Dez-mar-EST-ee-ah veer-EE-diss]
Common names: Stringy Acid Kelp
Phylum: Phaetophyta or Brown Algae
Where: in low intertidal to subtidal zone
Colour: light brown to red
Shape: finely branched, small round plump blades
Texture: smooth and rubbery
Size: 30 to 40 cm (12 to 15 inches) long
Notes: Most acidic of all kelp, it secretes sulfuric acid that can damage other species if they are collected in the same container.

Gravel and Cobblestone Beaches
Species Checklist:

☐	*Littorina scutulata*	Checkered Periwinkle
☐	*Littorina sitkana*	Sitka Periwinkle
☐	*Nucella emarginata*	Ribbed Dogwinkle
☐	*Nucella lamellosa*	Wrinkled Purple Whelk
☐	*Lirabuccinum dirum*	Dire Whelk
☐	*Petrolisthes eriomerus*	Porcelain Crab
☐	*Hemigrapsus oregonensis*	Green Shore Crab
☐	*Hemigrapsus nudus*	Purple Shore Crab
☐	*Pugettia gracilis*	Graceful Kelp Crab
☐	*Pugettia producta*	Northern Kelp Crab
☐	*Cancer productus*	Red Rock Crab
☐	*Cancer magister*	Dungeness Crab
☐	*Pagurus granosimanus*	Granular Hermit Crab
☐	*Pagurus hirsutiusculus*	Hairy Hermit Crab
☐	*Pinnixa subquadrata*	Pea Crab
☐	*Tealia crassicornis*	Northern Red Anemone
☐	*Anthopleura elegantissima*	Aggregating Sea Anemone
☐	*Anthopleura artemisia*	Green Burrowing Sea Anemone
☐	*Porphyra perforata*	Red Laver
☐	*Mastocarpus papillatus*	Turkish Towel
☐	*Costaria costata*	Seersucker
☐	*Laminaria saccharina*	Sugar Wrack
☐	*Desmarestia viridis*	Stringy Acid Kelp

SEASHORE EXPLORING LOG

Location: _____

_____

Date: _____

Shore Type: _____

Tide Level:

☐ High

☐ Mid

☐ Low

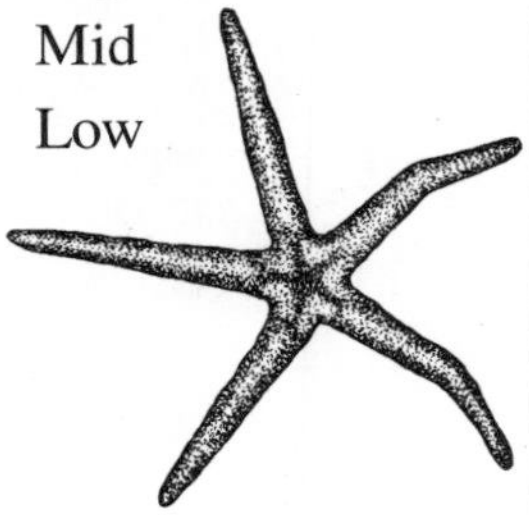

Plant and Animal Species

(observe the size and colour, where found in intertidal
region, and what other animals/plants are close by)

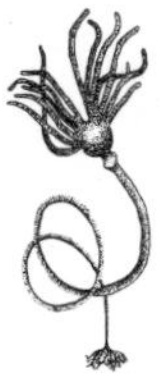

Vancouver Island Shores I

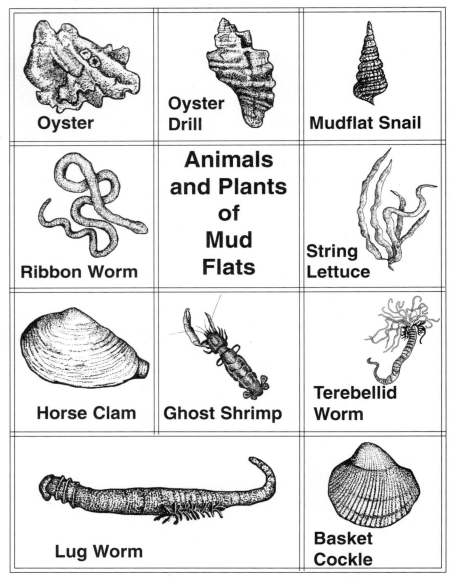

Oyster	**Oyster Drill**	**Mudflat Snail**
Ribbon Worm	**Animals and Plants of Mud Flats**	**String Lettuce**
Horse Clam	**Ghost Shrimp**	**Terebellid Worm**
Lug Worm		**Basket Cockle**

MUD FLATS AND SHORELINES NEAR RIVER ESTUARIES

The mud flat is often overlooked by the seashore explorer. At low tide, it appears to be void of life, and the sea air may have the unpleasant smell of rotting seaweed and detritus.

Very important to coastal ecosystem

Once considered a wasteland, the mud flat is now known to play an essential role in the coastal ecosystem. Mud flats provide a habitat for a large number and variety of marine creatures and plants. These creatures are very important to the marine food web.

A mud flat is found at the protected head of a long bay or at the mouth of a major river or creek that flows into the Strait. It is formed by river sediments that are carried into the Strait and mixed with the sand and gravel.

Rich in organic matter

With the lack of strong wave action and currents, the river sediments settle to the bottom. This mud is rich in decaying organic matter and is an excellent food source for many marine animals.

Life is below the surface

Animal life on the mud flat occurs predominately below the surface. Evidence of it can be seen on the surface where little heaps of ornately excreted mud and various holes and burrows are clearly visible.

On Mud Flats, Look For

1
Ghost Shrimp
2
Clam
3
Oyster
4
Oyster Drill
5
Ribbon Worm
6
Lug Worm
7
Thread Worm
8
Terebellid Worm
9
Sea Lettuce
10
Green String Lettuce

Species and natural history of these creatures and plants are described in this chapter.

Habitat for clams, oysters and worms

Known primarily as a habitat for clams, oysters and worms, intertidal zonation on the mud flat is not as evident as it is on a rocky or cobblestone shoreline. The zones occur below the surface of the mud rather than on it, invisible to the seashore explorer's eye.

Animals of the mud flat have adapted to compensate for the difficulties of breathing, moving and gathering food below the surface layer of mud.

Tips for exploring muddy shores

✪ Walking about the mud flat is difficult. The surface layer of mud retains so much water that it instantly liquifies when stepped on. The suction created under foot can quite literally suck the shoes off your feet. Wear tightfitting shoes to avoid losing them.

✪ Look for signs on the mud flat's surface which indicate that creatures are living below. Examine the shape and size of surface burrows and patterns of piles of fecal castings on the mud flat.

✪ Use your hands for digging and make sure all holes are filled in. If necessary, use a small garden claw with forked fingers. Avoid flat edged shovels that can cut off clam siphons when digging.

Some parks with mud flats

Most of the parks along the shoreline are not located in areas with mud flats. However, a few parks with muddy/sandy flats are:

Coles Bay Regional Park Victoria/Saanich Peninsula
Hecate Park Cowichan/Duncan
Goose Spit Regional Park Courtenay/Comox

More Animals To Look For On Mud Flats

Sea Anemone
Pea Crab
(inside clams)
Shore Crab

Species and natural history of these creatures are described in other chapters.

The Ghost Shrimp

The seashore explorer who discovers a ghost shrimp on the mud flat soon realizes why it received its common name. The exoskeleton or body covering is coloured a "ghostly" transparent whitish-pink. Softer and more pliable than the exoskeleton of other crustaceans, the thorax of the ghost shrimp is thicker or deeper than it is wide. Two pairs of antennae are clearly visible, its eyes are round and close set, mounted on stalks, and it has visibly hairy mouth parts.

Lives in J-shaped burrow

The ghost shrimp spends most of its life below the surface of the mud in a J-shaped burrow which it digs out using its mouth parts. It carries the sand and mud to the surface opening with its larger pincer and legs. The burrow can have many branches and be fairly complex with enough room for turning around. It is often used as a home by other intertidal creatures such as pea crabs and assorted small clams.

Plankton and detritus feeder

As it digs, the ghost shrimp eats much of the sand, straining out the detritus or organic material for its food. It also consumes microscopic plankton which it filters from the sea water that fills its burrows.

Reproduction is a year-round activity. Like crabs, female ghost shrimp carry the fertilized eggs under their abdomens on special flaps called swimmerets. The eggs hatch into free-swimming larvae.

The ghost shrimp, like all crustaceans, moults its exoskeleton in order to grow. Its gills are located at the side of the thorax in special chambers under the exoskeleton. The life span of the ghost shrimp has been estimated at several years.

The mud shrimp, a close relative to the ghost shrimp, is also a conspicuous inhabitant of the mud flat. Watch for moulted exoskeletons strewn among the debris at the high tide mark.

Did you know that...

the smell associated with low tide is the odour of decaying seaweed? Rotting seaweed generates the gas hydrogen sulphide, the smell often associated with sewage and rotting eggs. In the summer, when the direct sunlight breaks down the seaweed more quickly, the smell can be particularly strong.

111

Upogebia pugettensis

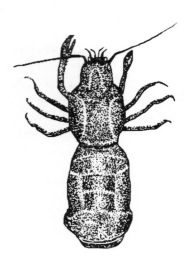

[You-poe-JEE-be-ah pew-jet-EN-sis]
Common name: Blue Mud Shrimp
Where: burrowing in sandy/muddy flats and in muddy gravel
Zone: middle to low intertidal
Colour: bluish/grey with light speckles on surface, hairy body particularly on legs
Pincers: flattened equal-sized claws, large tail fan often tucked under the body is used for swimming
Size: 15 cm (6 inches) long by 2.5 cm (1 inch) high
Notes: U-shaped burrow depth to 60 cm (23 inches) with two openings 60 to 90 cm (23 to 35 inches) apart. Its burrows do not have little piles of sand and fine gravel at the surface.

Neotrypaea californiensis

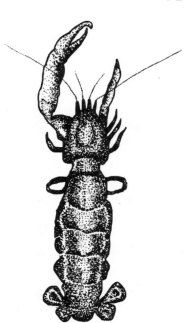

(=Callianassa californiensis)
[Knee-oh-try-PEE-ah kal-ee-FORN-ee-en-sis]
Common name: California Ghost Shrimp
Where: burrowing in mud flats and in pockets of sand on boulder/cobblestone beaches
Zone: high to low intertidal
Colour: salmon-pink/white colour with yellow swimmerets, almost transparent particularly on sides where gills are visible
Shape: long antennae, one huge pincer
Size: 10 cm (4 inches) long and about 2 cm (.8 inches) wide
Notes: Digs J-shaped burrow with larger pincer to depth of 60 cm (23 inches) from the surface. Piles of sand are heaped around the .7 cm (.5 inches) burrow opening. Reproduces year round.

The Bivalve: The Mollusk With Two Shells or Valves

Clams, cockles, oysters, mussels and even shipworms are all members of the class Bivalvia (formerly called Pelecypoda) within the Phylum Mollusca.

All bivalves live within two shells which are composed of calcium carbonate, a high concentration of salts.

The two shells are joined at the umbo by rounded tooth-like projections that act like a pivot and keep the two shells properly aligned. Between the projections is a very tough but flexible hinge ligament which strengthens the connection. Sometimes this ligament is visible on the exterior of the shell.

The shells of bivalves are broadly constructed in layers.

The first outer layer or periostracum, often yellow or brownish in colour, acts as a barrier between the corrosive elements in the sea water and the shell's inner layers.

The second layer is thick and hard, and has a chalky consistency. Concentric lines are marked in ridges that run parallel to the outer shell edge on most species of bivalves. Radial lines or ridges run toward the margin of the shell.

The third or inner layer is the nacre, where the build-up of many fine layers of iridescent calcium carbonate form mother-of-pearl.

Inside the bivalve shell, adductor muscles are used to open and close the two valves. Look for the scars where the adductor muscle was once attached inside empty shells.

Bivalves have two siphons that vary in length and shape according to the species. One siphon is used like a drinking straw to draw in sea water, while the other siphon is used to expel the bivalve's waste material and waste water. Some clams appear to have one enormous siphon, but two siphons are actually joined by fleshy material. Other bivalves have siphons that do not extend out of the shell.

Most bivalves have a foot that varies in size and use depending upon the species. Many bivalves use their foot to bury themselves to various depths in the sand and mud. For many stationary bivalves, almost all vestiges of a foot have been lost.

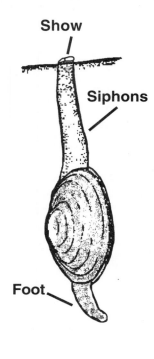

Show

Siphons

Foot

Chondrophore

Adductor Muscle Scar

The Clam

For many of us, picking up shells on the beach is an enjoyable part of seashore exploring. The variety of colours, shapes and sizes of clam shells seems endless.

Inside the live clam, a large mantle, an envelope made of very thin fleshy tissue, has folds or compartments which enclose the clam's organs. The curly edge of the mantle is visible when the valves are slightly open. Although a clam does not have a brain or head, it does have a nervous system that is sensitive to touch and light.

The ends of the clam's siphons are always exposed to the sea water. Called "show," the exposed parts often have unique fringes or are coloured.

As water passes over the clam's gills, dissolved oxygen is absorbed and various bits of floating food particles are sorted, trapped in mucous and transferred to the mouth. Clams reproduce through broadcast fertilization.

Tresus capax

[TRACE-us CAP-axe]
Common names: Horse or Gaper Clam
Where: mud/sand/gravel
Zone: low intertidal to subtidal
How deep: will burrow to 1 metre (39 inches) below surface; typical depth is 30 cm (12 inches)
Colour: yellowish-brown periostracum
Size: up to 18 cm (7 inches) long by 12 cm (4.7 inches) high (usually one and a half times long as high)

Shape: oval oblong
Siphons and Show: long, covered with dark rough skin; hard end covering on siphons looks like a walnut on surface sands
Shell texture: smooth shell with very fine concentric lines
Notes: Brown periostracum flakes off quickly after death. Spurts water when disturbed during low tide. Hosts pea crabs.

Clinocardium nuttallii

[Clin-oh-CARD-ee-um new-TAHL-ee]

Common name: Heart, Basket, or Nuttall's Cockle
Where: mud or sand/gravel bottoms
Zone: low intertidal to subtidal
How deep: found on surface
Colour: grey covered with yellowish-brown periostracum
Size: up to 14 cm (5.5 inches) long and 10 cm (4 inches) high
Shape: round or heart-shaped, plump heavy thick shell
Shell texture: coarse radiating ridges crossed by fine concentric growth lines
Siphons and Show: very short and ends fringed with white hairs
Notes: Sickle-shaped foot can be used by the cockle to jump and escape predators. Life span estimated at up to 15 years. Hosts pea crabs.

Saxidomus gigantea

(=*Saxidomus giganteus or Saxidomus nuttalli*)

[Sax-ee-DOE-muss jee-GANT-ee-ah]

Common name: Butter Clam
Where: sandy or cobblestone beaches
Zone: middle to low intertidal to subtidal
How deep: will burrow to 30 cm (12 inches) deep
Size: up to 13 cm (5 inches) long by 8 cm (3 inches) high
Colour: dull greyish-white shell, prominent brown/black hinge, interior not glossy, and stained with purple
Shape: very thick oblong oval
Shell texture: raised concentric ridges, no radiating lines
Siphons: long white siphons with separate black fringed tips
Notes: Tolerates brackish water. Shell gapes open slightly at posterior end. Life span to 20 years.

Mya arenaria

[MY-ah are-ee-NAR-ee-ah]
Common names: Mud or Soft-shell Clam
Where: muddy/sandy substrate near brackish water
Zone: low intertidal to subtidal 46 metres
How deep: burrows to 10 to 20 cm (4 to 8 inches)
Size: up to 10 cm (4 inches) long by 6 cm (2.4 inches) high
Shell texture: thin brittle shell that is easily broken, hinge ligament internal
Colour: chalky-white or grey
Shape: oval, rounded at front, pointed at rear; large socket hinge called chondrophore is visible on one valve
Siphons: fused, long with tough darker skin
Notes: Squirts stream of water at low tide when disturbed. Life span 10 to 12 years. An introduced species to local waters.

Macoma secta

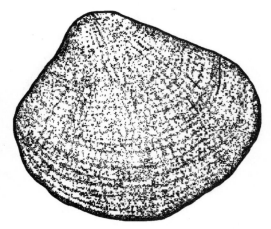

[Ma-KOE-mah SEC-tah]
Common name: White Sand or Butterfly Clam
Where: prefers clean sand
Zone: low intertidal to subtidal
How deep: 20 to 45 cm (8 to 18 inches) deep
Size: 9 cm (3.5 inches) long by 7 cm (2.8 inches) high
Shell: oval, one valve is smooth and flattened, while other is slightly inflated
Shell texture: diagonal ridges
Colour: white with shiny brownish/yellow flaking periostracum
Siphons: long, unequal in length and separate
Notes: A favourite food for Lewis' Moon Snail, *Polinices lewisi*. Often referred to as Butterfly Clam because empty open shells look like butterfly wings. Can be confused with Bent-nosed Clam, *Macoma nasuta*, but valves are not bent.

Venerupis philippinarum

*(=Tapes japonica, Tapes philippinarum,
Venerupis japonica, Ruditapes philippinarum)*
[Ven-er-OOP-us phil-eep-ee-NAR-um]
Common names: Japanese Littleneck or Manila
Clam
Where: gravel/muddy/sandy beaches
Zone: high to middle intertidal
How deep: lives on surface less than 10 cm (4
inches)
Size: up to 8 cm (3 inches) long by 6 cm (2.4 inches)
high
Shell texture: radial ridges more prominent than
concentric ridges; inside edge of shell is smooth
Colour: white with brown markings, yellow stains
with purple markings at siphon end on inside of shell
Shape: oblong shape and more elongated than
Protothaca staminea
Siphons: very short and fused with split tips
Notes: An introduced species.

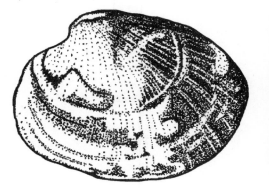

Protothaca staminea

[Pro-toe-THACK-ah stam-ee-NEE-ah]
Common name: Native or Pacific Littleneck Clam
Where: mud/sand or in fine gravel mixed with sand
Zone: high to low intertidal
How deep: on surface less than 10 cm (4 inches) deep
Size: up to 7 cm (2.8 inches) long by 5.5 cm
(2.2 inches) high
Shape: oval, plump valves equal in size
Shell texture: radiating ridges crossed by many concentric lines on thick shell; ligament clearly seen
Colour: whitish/tan with angular brown markings
Siphons: fused and extremely short
Notes: Life span is 14 years. *Protothaca staminea* is distinguished
from the Japanese Littleneck Clam, *Venerupis philippinarum*, by
the fine teeth on the inside edge or margin of its shell.

Macoma nasuta

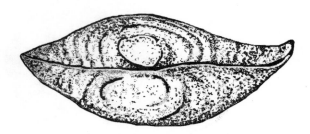

[Ma-KOE-mah nah-SUE-tah]
Common name: Bent-nosed Clam
Where: lives in muddy/sandy beaches, brackish or polluted waters
Zone: low intertidal to subtidal
How deep: 10 to 15 cm (4 to 6 inches) deep
Size: up to 7 cm (2.8 inches) long and 5 cm (2 inches) high
Shape: oval, flattened, with valves at one end bending to one side
Shell texture: thin flaking periostracum, some concentric ridges
Colour: white with yellowish periostracum

Nuttallia obscurata

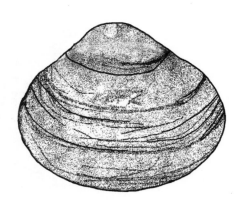

[Nut-all-EE-ah ob-skur-A-tah]
Common name: Varnish Clam, Dark Mahogany Clam
Where: mud or sand/gravel bottoms
Zone: high to middle intertidal
How deep: buried to 20 cm (8 inches)
Colour: yellow-brown periostracum, purple interior
Size: up to 5 cm (2 inches) long
Shape: oval, flat
Shell texture: glossy and smooth with flaking periostracum
Siphons: long and separate
Notes: Introduced species.

Red Tide and HABs (Harmful Algal Blooms)

"Red tide" is the common name used to describe the rapid growth of microscopic algae (phytoplankton) that often colour the coastline waters with a rusty red stain.

It is often erroneously associated with paralytic shellfish poisoning or PSP, but not all plankton that produce red-stained waters are toxic, and many toxic-producing plankton or HABs (Harmful Algal Blooms) do not produce any colour in the water. Harvesters of bivalves should be aware that the lack of red tide does not indicate it is safe to eat shellfish.

In the spring months, the surface waters of the Strait of Georgia warm and the nutrient-rich water from the deep rush to the surface. These conditions promote rapid growth of phytoplankton.

One species called *Alexandrium sp.* produces a reddish-brown coloured oil to keep afloat. When local waters become so saturated with the algae, the water becomes red and murky.

As a by-product of photosynthesis, *Alexandrium sp.* produces a saxitoxin. Bivalves, like the clam and mussel, which filter the algae-rich water through their bodies, accumulate the toxin in their organs. Although the clams are not harmed, any mammal or bird that eats the infected shellfish can be poisoned.

Paralytic shellfish poisoning in humans can cause total muscular paralysis and eventually death (when the lungs cease to function). Artificial respiration and immediate hospitalization are required.

There is no associated taste or smell to the toxin and cooking the infected shellfish will not remove it. Laboratory tests are the only sure way to determine the safety of eating shellfish.

Fisheries and Oceans Canada monitors toxicity levels of shellfish weekly along the east coast of Vancouver Island throughout the summer months. When levels of toxicity become potentially dangerous, the infected beaches are closed to shellfish harvesting. Notices are placed at beaches, in tourist and park information centres, and in local newspapers.

Call (604) 666-2828 for current Fisheries and Oceans Shellfish and Red Tide Update.

Did you know that...
the first recorded case of shellfish poisoning in local waters was in 1793 when the crew of Captain George Vancouver's ship ate tainted mussels from the Strait of Georgia?

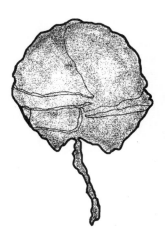

Microscopic
Alexandrium sp.

The Oyster

The oyster is the basis of a valuable aquaculture industry on the east coast of Vancouver Island.

Oyster farms along east coast and Gulf Islands

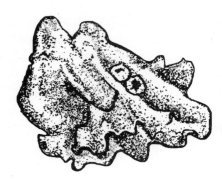

Many of the beaches, particularly on Hornby and Denman Islands, are sites of oyster and clam farms. Signs on the beach and red cement blocks in the intertidal region indicate the boundaries of an oyster or clam lease.

Seashore explorers should not wander along these beach properties, particularly during low tide, since walking can destroy the oysters and clams. Strict government regulations prohibit shellfish digging in these marked areas.

Valves are different sizes

The oyster's two valves or shells vary in size. These shells can be markedly variable, even within the same species. The lower or left valve is usually saucer shaped and most often cemented to a hard surface. The right or upper valve is more flat, larger and usually fluted or frilly.

Attaches to hard surface

The oyster larva or spat attaches itself to a hard surface by secreting a quick drying cement from a special gland. As the oyster grows larger, it continues to secrete cement to bond its shell to the hard surface. Over a number of years, oysters can become cemented to each other, creating large oyster reefs.

Lacks external siphons

The oyster lacks external siphons and feeds by filtering phytoplankton from the sea water. The oyster is very tolerant of brackish water and seashore explorers will often find oysters living in areas near fresh water drainage.

Ability to change gender

Rather than remain one gender all its life, the oyster is capable of changing from male to female and vice versa on an annual or biannual basis. This process is called alternating hermaphroditism.

Being a female one year and a male the next is an adaptive behaviour based on both genetic and environmental factors. By alternating gender, the sedentary oyster population insures that there will always be an adequate mix of sperm and eggs to continue the species.

Like other bivalves, the oyster reproduces by broadcast fertilization.

Did you know that... all bivalves can produce pearls but very few are large enough or of good enough quality to be of any economic value?

True or false: inedible in "r"-less months

Oyster epicures in the northern hemisphere have known for centuries that it is taboo to eat oysters in the "r"-less months. The breeding season, May to August, just happens to occur in the months of the year without the letter "r." According to connoisseurs, the oyster tends to be soft, mushy and lacking in flavour during the spawning season.

Native oyster is disappearing

The native Olympia Oyster, *Ostrea conchapila (=Ostrea lurida),* was once a common inhabitant of local waters. Like most oysters, it preferred to inhabit areas near fresh water seepage. Unfortunately, harmful toxins from pulp mill runoff were dumped into the Strait of Georgia via fresh water streams. Scientists believe these toxins caused the disappearance of the Olympia Oyster.

Introduced oysters

Most of the large edible oysters found on local beaches are descendants of the Pacific Oyster, *Crassostrea gigas,* which was introduced to local waters at the turn of the century. The Atlantic Oyster, *Crassostrea virginica*, was also introduced but failed to become established in the wild.

Shore birds like the oyster catcher, and animals such as the river otter, sea star, moon snail and oyster drill prey on the oyster.

Crassostrea gigas

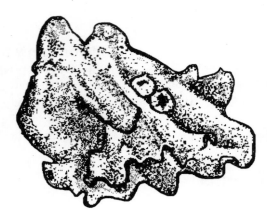

[Krass-OH-stree-ah JEE-jas]
Common name: Pacific or Japanese Oyster
Where: attached to rocks and shells in muddy substrate but will tolerate all kinds of substrates
Zone: middle intertidal to subtidal
Colour: greyish white with purple tinges
Shape: extremely variable, can be long and thin or round and deep, ridges are very prominent, usually highly irregular
Size: up to 30 cm (12 inches) long by 12 cm (4.8 inches) high
Notes: Introduced intentionally from Japan at turn of the last century.

Pododesmus cepio

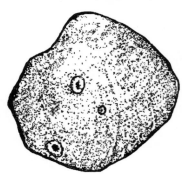

(=*Pododesmus macroschisma*)
[Poe-doe-DES-muss see-PEE-oh]
Common name: Rock Oyster, Blister or Jingle Shell Oyster
Where: on rocks, shells, dock pilings
Zone: low intertidal to subtidal
Colour: greyish white, sometimes tinged with green algae
Shape: irregularly circular depending upon substrate with variable radiating ridges
Size: to 13 cm (5 inches) long by 13 cm (5 inches) wide
Notes: From the Family Anomiidae which is not a true oyster. Appears to have only one thin shell. The flesh is bright orange. Attaches to substrate by byssus cap or plug which is visible on the surface of rocks long after the oyster has perished.

Introduced Species of Marine Animals and Plants

There are many non-native or introduced species of marine plants and animals that inhabit the Strait of Georgia. Many were intentionally cultivated, but most were accidentally introduced.

Scientists have determined that some non-native species, still in their juvenile or larval form, were dumped in the Strait of Georgia from ballast tanks of large foreign freighters. Other species were introduced inadvertently with species that were purposely introduced.

For example, the Pacific Oyster, *Crassostrea gigas*, was intentionally brought to local waters and is a great benefit to the local aquaculture economy. The long-term ecological impact of the Pacific Oyster is still of concern to some scientists.

Sargassum Seaweed

Other introduced species discussed in *Vancouver Island Shores I* are:

Mya arenaria, Soft-shell Clam
Venerupis philippinarum, Japanese Littleneck Clam
Nuttallia obscurata, Varnish Clam
Crassostrea gigas, Pacific Oyster
Sargassum muticum, Sargassum Seaweed

Japanese Littleneck Clam

Introduced Species

These two mollusks were introduced unintentionally in the Strait of Georgia with the Pacific Oyster.

Ceratostoma inornatum

(=Ocenebra japonica)
[Sar-ah-toe-STOW-ma in-or-NAT-um]
Common name: Japanese Oyster Drill
Where: oyster beds, gravel/mud/sand flats
Zone: middle to low intertidal
Colour: grey, inside stained purple
Shape: spindle plump, frilly
Size: up to 3 cm (1.2 inches) high by 1.6 cm (.6 inches) wide
Notes: It uses its specialized radula to rasp a neat little hole through the shells of oysters and other bivalves. A predator of both native and introduced mollusks, it retreats into mud in winter.

Batillaria cumingi

(=Batillaria attramentaria, Battillaria zonalis)
[Bat-eel-are-EE-ah come-IN-gee]
Common name: Mudflat Snail, False Cerith or Screw Shell
Where: sandy/muddy tidal flats, in brackish waters
Zone: high to middle intertidal
Colour: highly variable, usually grey with chocolate brown beads
Shape: long conical spire with 8 to 9 whorls
Size: 2.5 cm to 4 cm (1 to 1.6 inches) high by 1 cm (.4 inches) wide
Texture: beaded on surface
Notes: Life span up to 10 years.

The Marine Worm

Not many of us go to the seashore in search of marine worms. A worm is what you find on the beach when you are looking for something else. Worms are found in almost every type of beach substrate. They live in and amongst many attached animals such as mussels and in and amongst seaweed.

Major food source for intertidal animals

These bountiful creatures should not be underestimated in their importance in the intertidal scene. They are a major food source and an important link in the food web of many marine animals.

Since most species do not have common names, seashore field guides often list worms by the phylum, class or subclass, order or family name. References to polychaete worm, annelid worm, and nereid worm are often discussed in reference to the same worm. It can be very confusing for the novice seashore explorer to sort out which is what.

Two major groups of worms encountered

In very general terms, there are two common phyla of worms that the seashore explorer will encounter in the intertidal zone.

**Fecal Casting
of Marine Worm**

The Nemertean or Ribbon Worm

Phylum Nemertea [nee-mare-TEA-ah]

With soft, unsegmented, smooth, flat bodies, nemertean or ribbon worms look like threads or ribbons crawling over mudflats at low tide. They are often beautifully, brightly coloured.

Slimy and fragile

Typically very slimy to touch, they vary in size from a few centimetres to many metres long. Nemertean worms are very fragile and when picked up will break apart in a process called spontaneous fragmentation. New worms often regenerate from the small broken pieces.

Carnivores that capture prey with proboscis

Mostly carnivorous, ribbon worms possess a hollow muscular proboscis. The proboscis is shot out explosively through the mouth or a special opening and wrapped around it's prey. Speed is necessary to capture the swiftest of prey.

To discourage any attempt at escape, some nemertean species' proboscis has a coating of sticky mucous. Other nemertean worms have a proboscis with a piercing hook-like stylet that is loaded with potent toxin. The stylet is repeatedly stabbed into the flesh of the prey after which toxin is injected into the wound.

The proboscis is also used to burrow into sand and mud. The enlarged end of the proboscis is projected into the sediment and imbedded. The worm then pulls itself up toward its "anchored" proboscis.

Broadcast fertilizers

Nemertean worms generally have separate sexes and reproduce by broadcast fertilization. Spawning in warmer summer surface waters typically occurs at night.

Seashore explorers can find nemertean worms along muddy/sandy shores as well as along rocky shores, living in and amongst attached animals and seaweed.

Emplectonema gracile

[Em-pleck-tone-EE-ma Gra-SIL-ee]
Common name: Green Nemertean Worm
Where: on rocks in sediment between barnacles and mussels
Zone: middle intertidal
Shape: long and slender like a rubber band
Size: fully extended 15 to 20 cm (6 to 8 inches), contracted 2 or 3 cm (.8 to 1.2 inches)
Colour: dark to yellowish green with yellow underside
Notes: Occurs in great coiled masses. Preys on barnacles.

Paranemertes peregrina

[Pair-ah-nem-ERR-tess
 pair-ee-GREE-nah]
Common names: Mud Nemertean, Wandering Nemertean, Restless Worm
Where: muddy/sand amongst patches of Sea Lettuce, *Ulva sp.*, and amongst mussel beds
Zone: low intertidal
Colour: dark brown or purplish brown; underside is creamy yellow
Size: 25 cm (10 inches) long
Shape: head is semi-flattened and tail is pointed
Notes: Very active, crawls along on surface slime trails. Preys on annelid worms.

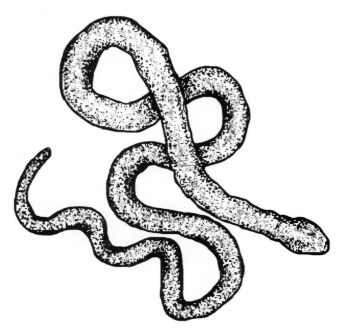

The Annelid or Segmented Worm

Phylum Annelida [an-el-EE-dah]

The second phylum of worms the seashore explorer is likely to encounter is the Annelida, the segmented worms.

Composed of identical segments

In general, each segment of an annelid worm's body, aside from its head or tail, is identical, having its own organs and nerve sites.

Polychaeta worms

Marine segmented worms are primarily in the Class Polychaeta [paul-ee-KEY-tah], which means many bristles in Greek. Each segment of the polychaete's body has side flaps called parapodia. They move or flap like oars to help the worm burrow in sand or mud or to swim about in the sea water.

Most polychaete worms have separate sexes and reproduce through broadcast fertilization. A free-living larva floats in amongst the plankton before settling to the bottom.

Many polychaete worms have a proboscis which is used to capture prey as well as burrow into the sediment. Other species use the contraction and expansion of their segmented bodies to move about. Polychaete worms can be divided into two groups.

Worms that move

The Order Errantia [ee-RANT-shuh] comprises those polychaete annelids that can move, swim or crawl. Some members of this polychaete order excavate elaborate burrows by eating their way through soft sediment, passing the sand through their bodies and depositing it at the surface in round ornate piles.

The polychaete worm, by dilating its segmented muscular body, creates a constant water current through its burrow which keeps its bushy gills oxygenated.

Help aerate the muddy sediments

Polychaete worms till the beach sediment and help aerate the surface layers. In environmental studies, scientists study the worm's tissues to determine the level of toxins in beach sediments.

Sedentary worms

The Order Sedentaria [said-ent-TARE-ee-ah] includes sedentary annelid worms that spend their lives within a tube of mud, sand, mucous or calcareous materials.

Rather than having a proboscis, many species of sedentary Polychaete have elaborate feathery tentacles around their mouths which act as food catchers and gills.

See also:

Axiothella rubrocincta, the Bamboo Worm, in the chapter on "Sandy Beaches and Eelgrass Bed,"
Serpula vermicularis, the Calcareous Tube Worm, and
Eudistylia vancouveri, the Feather Duster Worm, in the chapter on "Floating Docks and Wharf Pilings."

Abarenicola sp.

[A-bare-en-ee-KOL-ah]
Common name: Lug Worm
Where: sand/muddy bottoms
Zone: low intertidal
Colour: variable, usually dark brown
Shape: long thin, swollen head that tapers toward the posterior end
Texture: rough swollen with visible segments, bristly gills on sides
Size: average 15 cm (6 inches) but up to 30 cm (12 inches) have been observed
Burrow: L-shaped with the posterior of the worm close to the surface
Notes: Uses proboscis to create burrow. Consumes sediment and extracts organic matter for food. Inorganic matter, mixed with mucous, is extruded out at surface of burrow into a spiral shaped mound. Dimples in sand surface also indicate burrow below.

Notomastus tenuis

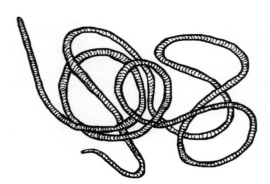

[No-toe-MAST-us TEN-you-iss]
Common name: Thread Worm
Where: mud and muddy/sand
Zone: low intertidal
Colour: dark red
Shape: very long and slender
Size: up to 20 to 30 cm (8 to 12 inches) long
Notes: Looks like thin earthworm with very tiny bristles. Extremely fragile and may be broken easily.

Thelepus crispus

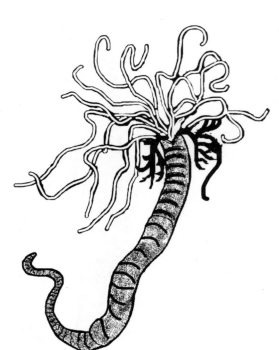

[Thay-LEE-pus KRIS-pus]
Common names: Curly Terebellid Worm, Hairy Gilled Worm
Where: underside of rocks, buried in muddy/sandy beaches
Zone: low intertidal
Colour: reddish-pink gills with white tentacles
Shape: tube is tough and sand-encrusted; three pairs of red gills, long slender tentacles are curly
Size: 15 cm (6 inches) long
Notes: Terebellid worms feed by extending long slender tentacles over the sandy/mud surface. Detritus is coated in mucous and transported up to the worm's mouth by cilia which line its groove-shaped or trough-like tentacles.

Seaweed

Mud flats are not particularly inviting to most seaweeds since there are so few hard surfaces on which the holdfasts can attach.

Ulva sp.

[OOL-vah]

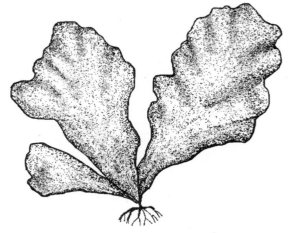

Common name: Sea Lettuce
Phylum: Chlorophyta or Green Algae
Where: low tidal zone, muddy/ sandy substrate
Colour: bright green, turns white or translucent when exposed to direct sunlight
Shape: thin broad blade arising from a disk-shaped holdfast
Texture: very fine sheets that look like crisp tissue paper when dried
Size: 10 to 15 cm (4 to 6 inches)
Notes: At low tide, covers areas of the mud flat like a green blanket.

Enteromorpha linza

[En-tear-oh-MORF-ah lin-ZAH]

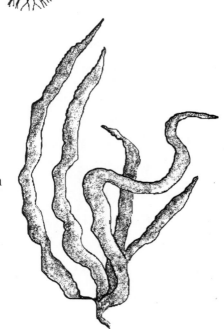

Common name: Green String Lettuce
Phylum: Chlorophyta or Green Algae
Where: middle to low intertidal, particularly near fresh water seepage
Colour: bright green
Shape: long flattened tubes which are ruffled at edges
Size: blades are 10 to 20 cm (4 to 8 inches) in length, 2 cm (.8 inches) in diameter
Texture: fine, delicate, turns white as it dries
Notes: It is often found under sheets of growing Sea Lettuce, *Ulva sp.* There are many species of *Enteromorpha* which are difficult to distinguish.

131

Mud Flats Species Checklist:

☐	*Upogebia pugettensis*	Blue Mud Shrimp
☐	*Neotrypaea californiensis*	California Ghost Shrimp
☐	*Tresus capax*	Horse Clam
☐	*Clinocardium nuttallii*	Heart Cockle
☐	*Saxidomus gigantea*	Butter Clam
☐	*Mya arenaria*	Soft-Shell Clam
☐	*Macoma secta*	White Sand Clam
☐	*Venerupis philippinarum*	Japanese Littleneck Clam
☐	*Protothaca staminea*	Native Littleneck Clam
☐	*Macoma nasuta*	Bent-nosed Clam
☐	*Nuttallia obscurata*	Varnish Clam
☐	*Crassostrea gigas*	Pacific Oyster
☐	*Pododesmus cepio*	Rock Oyster
☐	*Ceratostoma inornatum*	Japanese Oyster Drill
☐	*Batillaria cumingi*	False Cerith Shell
☐	*Emplectonema gracile*	Green Nemertean Worm
☐	*Paranemertes peregrina*	Mud Nemertean Worm
☐	*Abarenicola sp.*	Lug Worm
☐	*Notomastus tenuis*	Thread Worm
☐	*Thelepus crispus*	Curly Terebellid Worm
☐	*Ulva sp.*	Sea Lettuce
☐	*Enteromorpha linza*	Green String Lettuce

SEASHORE EXPLORING LOG

Location: _____

_____

Date: _____

Shore Type: _____

Tide Level:

☐ High

☐ Mid

☐ Low

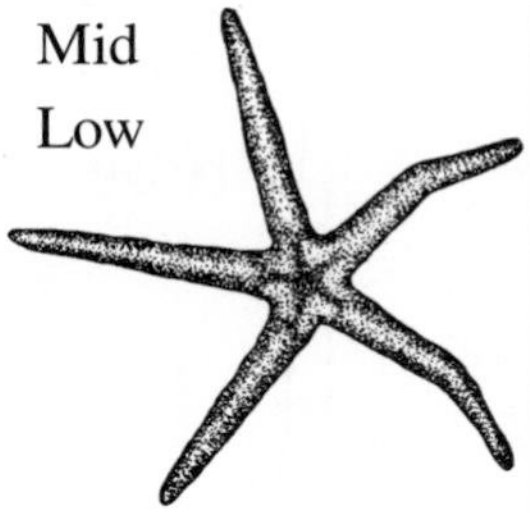

Plant and Animal Species

(observe the size and colour, where found in intertidal region, and what other animals/plants are close by)

Vancouver Island Shores I

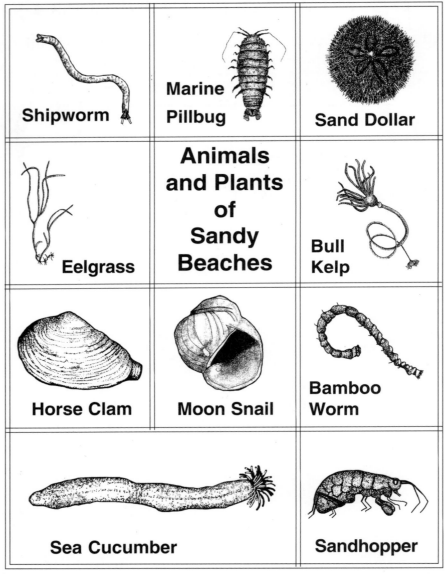

Shipworm	Marine Pillbug	Sand Dollar
Eelgrass	**Animals and Plants of Sandy Beaches**	Bull Kelp
Horse Clam	Moon Snail	Bamboo Worm
Sea Cucumber		Sandhopper

Vancouver Island Shores I

SANDY BEACHES AND EELGRASS BEDS

Small sandy shorelines along the east coast of Vancouver Island and in the Gulf Islands are typically found at the heads of shallow inlets and coves. The gentle lapping of waves brings fine particles of sand from deeper water. Since there is little wave action, the sand is rarely dragged out into the deeper waters of the Strait.

Glaciers created long sandy beaches

Long sandy beaches that stretch for a kilometre or more (half mile) are found along the east coast of Saanich Peninsula and from Parksville north to Comox/Campbell River area.

These magnificent sandy stretches of shoreline were created by the last ice age and take their present form from subsequent erosion. Around 15,000 years ago, the Frasier Glaciation (the most recent of at least three ice ages along this coast) ploughed southward across the Strait of Georgia toward Victoria.

As the huge glaciers moved over the land, deposits of sand and gravel were crushed beneath and caught in front of the advancing ice. When the glaciation process stopped, large deposits of sandy sediment were washed back toward the Strait in massive rivers of melting ice. Over time, when the level of water in the Strait and the coastline rebounded to its current level, the erosive effects of waves and tidal currents distributed these fine sands up and down the shoreline.

Mixture of sandy and muddy sediment

Many of the sandy beaches along the east coast of Vancouver Island are of mixed sediment, largely sand and mud. Back shores are narrow and sand dunes are nonexistent largely due to the lack of strong winds.

On Sandy Beaches, Look For

1 **Shipworm**
2 **Isopod**
3 **Amphipod**
4 **Bamboo Worm**
5 **Burrowing Sea Cucumber**
6 **Moon Snail**
7 **Sand Dollar**
8 **Bull Kelp**
9 **Eelgrass**
10 **Skeleton Shrimp**

Species and natural history of these creatures and plants are described in this chapter.

Life is below the surface

The constant movement of surface sand particles, created by the lapping of waves, provides little stability for plants and animals. Most intertidal creatures on sandy beaches have adapted by living under the surface. There, animals are protected from the action of waves and the risk of drying out at low tide. As well, exposure to changes in air temperature and water salinity diminishes below the surface. Most of the animals living on sandy beaches rarely emerge to the surface.

Eelgrass beds

Only a few plants such as eelgrass can anchor themselves in the shifting sand. Eelgrass is not an algae but a vascular land plant that grows in vast beds. Its roots and rhizomes stabilize the bottom and prevent the sand from being carried away. Within these massive root structures and tangled blades, decaying matter and silt accumulate, providing food and shelter for many marine animals.

Driftwood

Scattered along the sandy high tide line is an assortment of uprooted stumps and drift logs. Uprooted stumps originate in the rain coast forest and are carried down to the Strait by river currents. The stumps drift among the waves until they are cast up on shore. Drift logs have escaped from log rafts on their way to lumber and pulp and paper mills.

Driftwood is an integral part of the intertidal community. It often protects the finer particles of the beach from the impact of waves and tidal currents, and provides essential habitat and a source of food for many seashore creatures. Excessive numbers of drift logs may have a negative impact on the shoreline. They can batter rocky shores and hasten the natural process of erosion.

Some parks with sandy beaches

Island View Regional Park Saanich Peninsula
Rathtrevor Beach Provincial Park Parksville/Qualicum
Fillongley Provincial Park Denman Island
Miracle Beach Provincial Park Courtenay/Comox

More Animals To Look For On Sandy Beaches

**Gribble
Marine Pillbug
Sandhopper
Brooding Sea
Anemone**

Species and natural history of these creatures are described in this chapter.

The Shipworm

In amongst the scattered driftwood, the seashore explorer will find many logs riddled with circular tunnels about two centimetres (.8 inches) in diameter. These burrows, coated with a very thin white-coloured calcareous lining, were once the home of the shipworm, a creature known for its destructive habit of boring through and eroding submerged wood.

The shipworm is not really a worm. Although in adult form it has a wormlike appearance, this bivalve mollusk has two small sharp-edged valves near its head that it uses to tunnel through wood. By opening and closing its shells, the shipworm carves out a burrow excavated along the grain of the wood. No two burrows ever cross.

Like other bivalves, the shipworm is a plankton filter feeder. Two siphons are exposed outside the burrow's entrance; one draws in sea water and the other expels the used sea water and other wastes.

The shipworm is a broadcast fertilizer; males and females distribute their gametes into the open sea water. In the larval stage of its life cycle, the shipworm settles on a piece of submerged wood and begins the scraping process.

Bankia setacea

[Bank-EE-ah set-ah-SEE-ah]
Common names: Feathery Shipworm, Pacific Shipworm
Where: in submerged wood
Shape: wormlike with two white siphons
Burrow: up to 2.5 cm (1 inch) in diameter
Size: to .7 cm (.25 inches) wide and 1 metre (39 inches) long
Notes: Grasps sides of burrow with sucker-like foot. Abandoned shipworm burrows are used as habitat by other intertidal creatures. Common Shipworm, *Teredo navalis,* does not usually occur in local waters, although this species of shipworm from the Atlantic has been found in some locations along the Strait of Georgia.

137

The Isopod

The isopod, found on every kind of beach and in every zone of the intertidal region, is a small crustacean. There are so many different species of isopods along the shoreline that identification is difficult.

The isopod has a head that is fused onto a segmented body and legs that are all, more or less, uniform in size.

The body of the isopod is flattened from top to bottom and the segments tend to be small and fused together.

Small appendages called pleopods run along or under the thorax. The pleopods function as gills and as oars to paddle through the sea water.

Several species of isopods are known to be parasitic and can be found living on the gills of intertidal and subtidal fishes.

Limnoria lignorum

[Lim-NOR-ee-ah lig-NOR-um]
Common name: Gribble
Where: in wood pilings and docks, boats, drift logs still submerged in water
Shape: broad segmented body with eight pairs of legs
Size: about 3 mm (.12 inches) long
Colour: white
Notes: The gribble can wreak havoc on any submerged wooden surfaces much like the Shipworm, *Bankia setacea*. It burrows its way through the wood, deriving sustenance from the wood fibre. The excavated tunnels are interconnected and rarely go deeper than 2 cm (.8 inches) below the wood surface. Submerged surface wood becomes so eroded with gribble holes that it breaks off with wave action, revealing more wood surface for the gribble to attack. Gribble spreads to driftwood as a swimming adult rather than through the dispersal of free-drifting larvae as does the Shipworm, *Bankia setacea*.

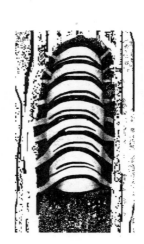

Cirolana harfordi

[Seer-oh-LAN-ah har-FORD-ee]
Common name: Marine Pillbug
Where: under debris and stones on all beaches, in mussel beds
Zone: high to low intertidal
Colour: greyish yellow or brown
Shape: elongate, oval and flattened, like the common garden pill bug
Size: 2 cm (.8 inches) long by 6 mm (.25 inches) wide
Note: An important intertidal scavenger of animal and plant tissues.

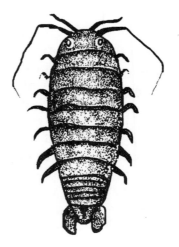

Idotea wosnesenskii

[Id-oh-TEA-ah was-ness-SEN-sky]
Common names: Rockweed Isopod, Vosnesensky's Isopod
Where: on rocky shores, in mussel beds, among seaweed
Zone: high to low intertidal
Colour: greenish yellow (blends in with colour of Rockweed, *Fucus sp.*)
Shape: elongated and flattened with seven pairs of legs
Size: 4 cm (1.6 inches) long by 1.5 cm (.6 inches) wide
Notes: Look amongst Rockweed, *Fucus sp.* Nocturnal scavengers that come out at night to feed on seaweed and dead animal matter.

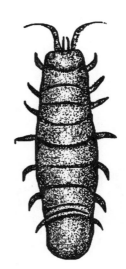

The Amphipod

On the sandy shore, the high tide water line is often marked by a ribbon of drying seaweed. Pick up a few fronds and watch the amphipods jump in every direction.

Amphipod means "different-sized foot" in Latin and the tiny crustacean's clawed legs are of varying sizes. The longer rear legs, or pleopods, are used primarily for jumping. Many species of amphipods are able to leap up to a metre (3 feet) in distance.

The amphipod has a segmented body that is hunched over or compressed from side to side. The most common and conspicuous amphipod to be found along our shores is the sandhopper or beach flea.

Burrows in sand

The sandhopper excavates small burrows in the sand with its front appendages. The burrow entrance can be seen on the surface sand and is typically less than 5 mm (.2 inches) in diameter.

Mating occurs between male and female typically within the burrow, and eggs are brooded in a special sac along the female's thorax. Eggs develop into tiny adult-shaped sandhoppers. There is no larval or free-swimming stage in the life cycle of the sandhopper.

Did you know that...
during the night, the amphipod leaves its burrow to feed on seaweed and any dead animal matter washed ashore? As dawn approaches, the scavenger returns to its burrow or takes refuge under decaying seaweed cast up on shore.

Traskorchestia traskiana

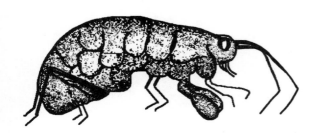

(=*Orchestia traskiana*)
[Tras-core-KEYS-tea-ah tras-KEY-an-ah]
Common name: Sandhopper, Beach Flea, Kelp Flea
Where: sand beaches, in cast-up drying seaweed
Zone: high intertidal
Colour: dull grey or brown
Shape: arched, stout, jointed with antennae
Size: up to 2 cm (.8 inches) long, 5 mm (.2 inches) wide
Notes: Can swim on its flattened sides.

The Bamboo Worm

During low tide, look very closely on the sand surface for small tubes of mud or sand sprouting up all over the intertidal region. Occasionally, as the tidal waters rush away from the shore, drifting strands of seaweed and eelgrass get caught on the erect tubes, making them more conspicuous.

These tubes are the home of the segmented sedentary tube worm. The small tubes are typically made from the soft mud and sand mixed with the worm's mucous.

For more details about marine worms, please refer to the chapter on "Mud Flats."

Axiothella rubrocincta

[Axe-ee-oh-THELL-ah rube-roe-SINK-tah]
Common name: Bamboo Worm
Where: sandy to muddy/sand bottoms; tolerates brackish water
Zone: low intertidal
Shape: slender and round
Size: up to 15 cm (6 inches) long
Colour: green with red bands on the fourth to eighth segments
Burrow: brittle sandy tube about 3 mm (.15 inches) in diameter. It is possible to dig carefully to 15 cm (6 inches) deep to see the intact tube below surface.
Notes: Eats detritus, mud and sand, extracting organic material. The green colour is a result of eating algae present in mud.

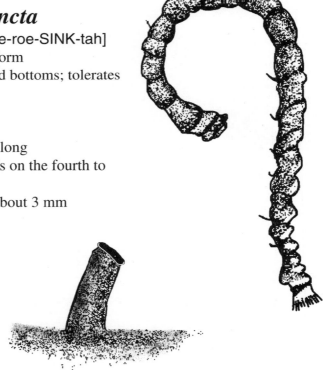

141

The Sea Cucumber

Many novice seashore explorers are amazed, puzzled and intrigued upon their first encounter with a sea cucumber.

Very low intertidal zone dweller

The sea cucumber lives at the very low intertidal to the subtidal zones of our shores, usually under rocks or buried in soft sediment.

It is not difficult to imagine what it looks like. Its common name describes its shape: cylindrical and plump. The stout sea cucumber's interior cavity is filled with sea water giving many species an almost over-inflated appearance when immersed in water.

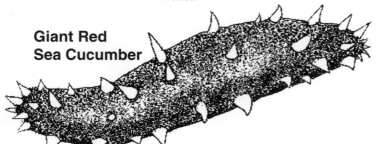

Giant Red Sea Cucumber

At low tide, a sea cucumber discovered under a rock may resemble a deflated, wrinkled balloon. The creature's internal fluids slowly leak out through its anus when not submerged.

Related to the sea star and sand dollar

As a member of the Phylum Echinodermata, sea cucumbers have tube feet that operate exactly like those of the sea star, except that the madreporite or opening valve to the sea water is located inside the sea cucumber's body rather than on its external body surface.

Tube feet used to attach to hard surfaces

Some species of sea cucumbers have rows of stiff non-retractable tube feet around their bodies, while others have them only on their lower surface. Tube feet are used primarily to attach to rocks and other hard surfaces and provide some movement.

Soft, muscular body

The soft, muscular body of the sea cucumber has an advantage over its stiff echinoderm relative, the sea star. The sea cucumber can move about by contracting and expanding its body, much like a worm does. With such a malleable body, some species of sea cucumbers squeeze under rocks, with only their fore and aft exposed to the water.

The sea cucumber's skin has no spines, cilia or pedicellaria. Its skin is tough and somewhat leathery to the touch. The California Sea Cucumber, *Parastichopus californicus*, has what look like dangerous spikes on its aboral or upper side, but they are purely cosmetic.

> **Sea Cucumber Facts**
> **Species:** 34 in Pacific Northwest
> **Food:** eats free-floating plankton or detritus collected on sticky tentacles around the mouth
> **Reproduction:** broadcast fertilization
> **Life span:** estimated at 5 to 10 years
> **Notes:** Eviscerates its internal organs; gills are located inside the anal opening

Tentacles surround its mouth

Although lacking a head, the sea cucumber has a circle of feeding tentacles surrounding its mouth. The number and shape of these modified tube feet vary according to the species. The tentacles are covered with a sticky mucous that are used either to brush or sweep the sea bottom for organic matter or to sway in the surrounding water for bits of floating plankton. Either way, the meticulous sea cucumber transfers the caught food to its mouth, licking each tentacle clean one at a time.

Breathing through its anal opening

At the opposite end of the sea cucumber is the anal opening. Branched respiratory trees or gills extend almost the entire length of the sea cucumber's internal body cavity. The sea cucumber draws or sucks sea water into the anal opening, bathes its gills, and then expels the used water and other waste materials out through the anus.

Bottom dwellers

Many sea cucumbers are bottom dwellers, known to be able to survive in extremely deep water where oxygen levels are poor. The sea cucumber is able to regulate the amount of oxygen passing over its gills by increasing the rate at which it draws and expels sea water.

Spewing out its internal organs

Some species of sea cucumbers are notorious for the annual habit of spewing their internal organs out through their anal opening. The reason for evisceration, as the process is called, is not fully understood.

One theory suggests it may be a defense mechanism. In order to escape from an approaching predator, the sea cucumber ejects its internal organs and rapidly moves away. The forfeited guts are eaten by the predator. A second theory suggests that parasites growing in the sea cucumber's internal organs can be quickly and effectively eliminated through annual evisceration. A third theory suggests that evisceration may reduce the cucumber's metabolic rate during its winter dormancy.

Fortunately for the sea cucumber, growing new internal organs takes only one to three months. During that period, the sea cucumber lives in a more or less dormant state, surviving on nutrients stored in its body walls.

Broadcast fertilizer

Most species of sea cucumbers are broadcast fertilizers. Separate sexes expel eggs and sperm into the sea water. Fertilized eggs develop into larvae that drift about with the plankton before settling to the bottom.

Commercially harvested

The only species of sea cucumber that is commercially harvested in local waters is the Giant Red Cucumber, *Parastichopus californicus*.

See also:

In the chapter on "Rocky Shores and Tidepools," see also:
Cucumaria miniata, Red Burrowing Sea Cucumber,
Eupentacta quinquesemita, White Sea Cucumber,
Parastichopus californicus, Giant Red Cucumber.

Tips for finding sea cucumbers

- ✪ Lift up large boulders and rocks gently to find attached sea cucumbers underneath.
- ✪ Look near areas where the water current runs quickly.
- ✪ During the months of late May to early July, when daylight low tides are at the lowest of the year, the very lowest of the low intertidal zone is accessible. This is the best time of the year to search for the sea cucumber.

Leptosynapta clarki

[Lep-toe-sigh-NAP-tah CLARK-ee]

Common name: Burrowing Sea Cucumber
Where: in muddy sand and gravel and among eelgrass beds
Zone: low intertidal
Colour: translucent white with some pink/orange tinges
Shape: wormlike with 11 to 13 small retractable tentacles
Size: 5 to 6 cm (2 to 2.4 inches) long when extended with a diameter of 1.5 to 2.5 cm (.6 to .9 inches)
Notes: Lacks tube feet and can be mistaken for a worm. It eats sand/mud, absorbing organic materials found there. Has tiny hooks on skin that stiffen and anchor its body.

The Moon Snail

During the early summer months, grey-coloured rings that look like the ends of discarded bathroom plungers are scattered about the low intertidal regions of the sandy beach. These sand collars are the egg cases of the moon snail.

Largest snail on our shores

The moon snail is the largest snail on our shores; the thick spiral shell can reach size of up to 12 cm (4.75 inches) in height. Its shell appears as one large whorl with five or more smaller whorls forming a spire.

Enormous foot

The foot of the moon snail is so fleshy and large that those who have taken to eating the gastropod prepare it by cutting it into steaks! When fully extended, the foot is the diameter of a dinner plate and can be as thick as 13 cm (5 inches).

It is difficult to imagine how the moon snail manages to withdraw its foot into its shell, but it does so by excreting water out of perforations around the foot edge and closing its operculum door. The moon snail cannot remain in this contracted state for long.

Plows below surface sand

The solitary moon snail is found just below the sand surface, about 5 to 10 cm (2 to 4 inches), plowing along in search of its next meal. It moves by millions of surface cilia beating along the enormous foot. If the animal needs to move quickly, it does so by the muscular wave contraction of its foot.

Carnivore uses its radula

As a carnivore, the moon snail consumes clams, oysters and other moon snails by either suffocating them with its large foot, or by drilling a hole through the prey's shell with its radula, extending its proboscis and eating the flesh.

Did you know that...
the small round hole drilled through the beak or umbo of a clam shell was likely created by a hungry moon snail? It (and other drilling gastropods) drill the hole with their radulas to gain access to the flesh inside.

Hole Drilled By Radula

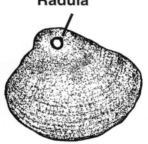

Eggs extruded and mixed with sand

Separate sexes copulate. Through a slit that encircles the foot, the female extrudes a sheet of mucous-coated eggs that are instantly coated in sand. The sheet is shaped by the outline of the snail's foot and shell. The snail moves away and detaches itself from the egg collar. From the diameter of the egg cases, the seashore explorer can accurately determine the size of the moon snail.

The sand collar, which can contain up to half a million eggs, slowly deteriorates and the planktonic larvae float away in the tidal currents.

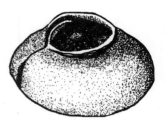

**Egg Case or
Sand Collar**

Polinices lewisii

(=Lunatia lewisii)
[Paul-ee-NIE-seas lu-EE-see]
Common name: Lewis' Moon Snail
Where: sandy and sandy/mud bottom
Zone: low intertidal to subtidal
Colour: tan or cream with thin slightly darker brownish periostracum
Shape: globe-shaped with four to five whorls
Size: Shell up to 14 cm (5.5 inches) high and 12 cm (4.7 inches) wide; mantle fully extended can be up to 30 cm (12 inches) wide and 13 cm (5 inches) high
Notes: Fleshy darker yellow mucous-covered mantle. It prefers to eat the Native Littleneck Clam, *Prothaca staminea,* and the Butter Clam, *Saxidomus gigantea.* The Sunflower Star, *Pycnopodia helianthoides,* other moon snails and river otters are its major predators.

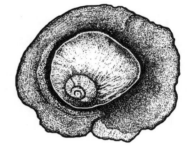

**Upper View of
Moon Snail With
Foot Extended**

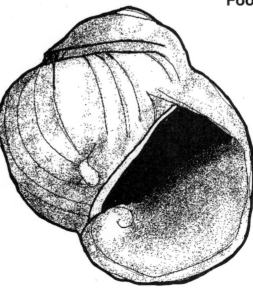

The Sand Dollar

Related to the sea urchin, sea star and sea cucumber, the sand dollar is completely flat and covered with soft purple-black, fur-like spines. Seashore explorers often find the bleached-white skeletons of dead sand dollars cast up on shore and are surprised by their live appearance.

Did you know that...

the rattle heard when dry sand dollar tests are shaken originates from the animal's complex feeding apparatus called Aristotle's Lantern? This feeding organ is composed of many fine teeth and calcium carbonate parts that rattle when dried out.

Five petal-shaped design

On the back of the dead disk or test, a five petal-shaped design is clearly visible. The pattern is created by tiny little holes from which the sand dollar's tube feet emerge.

Prefer to be right-side up

Due to the difficulty of turning itself over, and the need to be oral or mouth-side down, the sand dollar is rarely found high up in the intertidal zone, where breaking waves may knock it over and the effects of direct sunlight during low tide may dry it out.

The sand dollar stands on an angle with one third or more of its disk buried in the sand. In this position, the sand dollar feeds on plankton and bits of algae that it catches on its mucous-covered spines. The food particles are transported along a food tract toward its mouth via cilia and tube feet. Its mouth is located in the middle of its oral side. Gills are found around the mouth area.

Eats sand grains for anchorage

During low tide, the sand dollar uses its movable spines to dig itself under surface sands to protect itself from tidal currents. Smaller sand dollars eat heavy sand grains like iron oxide and this additional weight helps anchor them in the surface sands.

By the time the sand dollar reaches its adult size, however, the extra weight is no longer required and the grains that were stored in the gut are ejected.

Found in congregations

Sand dollars are often found in groups along sandy shores, and this congregating behaviour enhances reproduction. Sand dollars are of separate sexes and broadcast fertilizers. Eggs or sperm are discharged from a duct at the top centre of the disk. Eggs are fertilized at random and develop into free-swimming larvae.

Spawning occurs in the summer months, and individuals appear to breed repeatedly within this period. The larvae drift in the plankton, finally taking an adult form and settling to the bottom.

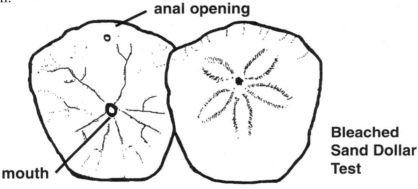

anal opening

mouth

Bleached
Sand Dollar
Test

Dendraster excentricus

[Den-DRAS-ter ex-sen-TRICK-us]
Common name: Eccentric Sand Dollar
Where: sand bottoms
Zone: low intertidal to subtidal
Colour: dark purple-black
Shape: disk-shaped, flattened on one edge
Texture: velvety fine spines
Size: up to 7 cm (2.8 inches) in radius and .6 cm (.25 inches) thick
Notes: Eccentric refers to the petal-shaped pattern which is just off centre.

149

Ripple and Swash Marks

Identifying the various marks along the beach can be fun. It has been said that the sandy beach can be read like a book. It can tell you if the tide is falling or rising from the various swash and rill marks left behind on the sand. Different holes and deposits on the sand can reveal what animals live below, and the webbed foot prints along the surface can tell you what shore birds have been strolling about.

Swash Marks On Surface Sands

Under water marks

Backwash ripples in the sand look like small waves and troughs created by tidal currents. If the side of the ripple on the Strait side is steeper than the ripple facing toward the beach, the tide is rising. If the ripple is steeper on the side facing the beach, the tide is falling.

Rill marks are produced by water draining from a beach during a falling tide. They are small erosional features that resemble draining patterns perpendicular to the shoreline.

Swash marks are irregular thin wavy lines or ridges of fine sand, foam and bits of seaweed and debris that form at the leading edge of the wave. Swash marks typically indicate the location of the last high tide line.

Surface marks

Sand ripples are generated by coastal winds above the high water mark. A miniature wind-shadow ridge is formed in the lee of driftwood, pebbles, shells or other objects with the axis aligned parallel to the prevailing wind direction. Other surface marks include holes in sand created by clams and ghost shrimp, and decorative fecal deposits from polychaete worms.

Fecal Deposits On Surface Sands

Seaweed

In general, the moving sediments of the sand beach do not provide a firm enough substrate for a seaweed's holdfast to attach. Often cast up on the sandy shore, however, are the long whiplike stipes of the subtidal Bull or Ribbon Kelp.

Nereocystis leutkeana

[Ner-ee-oh-SIS-tis lute-key-AN-ah]
Common name: Bull or Ribbon Kelp
Phylum: Phaetophyta or Brown Algae
Where: subtidally anchored 9 to 15 metres (30 to 50 feet) below the water surface
Colour: shiny brown
Shape: stipe is long hollow leathery whiplike with cylindrical air bladder or bulb filled with air and carbon monoxide
Size: Subtidally up to 20 metres (65 feet) long. Cast-up intertidal specimens usually 1 to 2 metres (3 to 6.5 feet) in length.
Notes: The blades are held at the surface by an air bladder. Intertidally, juvenile bull kelp are often found washed up on a sandy shore, particularly after a storm. Grows at a rate of 14 cm (5.5 inches) per day in July and August in optimum conditions. This species lives only one year, develops in the spring and dies off in the succeeding winter.

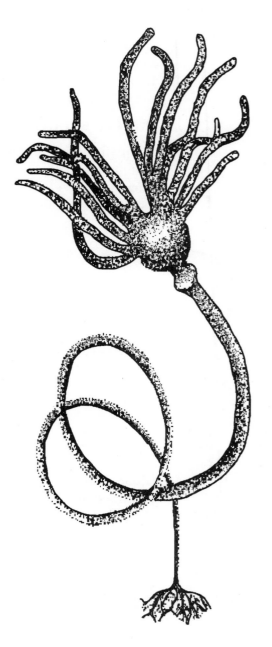

Eelgrass Beds

Eelgrass is not a seaweed or alga but an underwater perennial marine plant. It has roots, leaves, a plain green flower that is hidden beneath a transparent leaf sheath, and grows as tall as 1.5 metres (4.5 feet). Threadlike pollen is carried through the water and pollination takes place by chance.

Prefers sandy/muddy bottoms

Eelgrass requires clear water and plenty of sunlight to grow, so it prefers shallow sandy/muddy bottoms not much deeper than about 8 metres (26 feet). Usually eelgrass spreads its rhizomes and roots over a large area, forming huge thick mats.

Important role in seashore ecology

Although eelgrass is eaten by many herbivorous marine animals and migrating water fowl, it also plays an important role in seashore ecology as a provider of habitat and harbourer of decaying plant and animal matter.

Eelgrass protects sandy/muddy shores from the erosive effects of waves by slowing the movement of water. Sand sediment and decaying animal and plant matter are allowed to settle in amongst the roots and rhizomes rather than be carried out into the Strait. This provides food for a large number of marine animals.

Zostera marina

[Zoss-TAIR-ah mar-EE-nah]
Common name: Eelgrass
Where: bottom is a mixture of sand and mud
Zone: very low intertidal to subtidal
Colour: pale green
Shape: long thin bright green grasslike blades
Size: up to 1 metre (39 inches) long
Notes: Often found uprooted and either floating around docks or mixed up in debris.

Animals and plants living in eelgrass

In amongst the eelgrass beds, you are bound to see numerous kelp crabs and small fish that migrate in from the subtidal regions to feast on the various animals found inhabiting the eelgrass beds.

Epiactis prolifera
[Ee-pee-ACT-iss pro-liff-URR-ah]

Common name: Brooding Anemone
Where: on eelgrass leaves, seaweed fronds or occasionally on rocks
Zone: low intertidal to subtidal
Colour: tentacles are brown to greenish brown although various colours from red to green have been reported; oral disk often has radiating white lines on it
Size: 2.5 cm (1 inch) high to 5 cm (2 inches) wide
Notes: Eggs develop inside the parent and growing larvae migrate out of their parent's oral disk, attaching themselves to the parent's stalk. Around 5 mm (0.2 inches) high, the tiny anemones move away to mature. Parents apparently breed all year round and can have up to thirty young attached at one time. Predators include the Leather Star, *Dermasterias imbricata,* and the Shaggy Mouse Nudibranch, *Aeolidea papillosa.*

Caprella laeviuscula
[Cap-RELL-ah lee-view-SKEW-lah]

Common name: Skeleton Shrimp
Where: on eelgrass, in hydroids attached to docks
Colour: variable, white to transparent or greenish to match eelgrass
Shape: long slender amphipod crustacean
Size: 5 cm (2 inches) long by 6 mm (.25 inches) wide
Notes: Looks like a miniature Praying Mantis. When feeding, it clings to the eelgrass by claws on its three pairs of hind legs.

Sandy Beaches and Eelgrass Beds
Species Checklist:

☐ *Bankia setacea* — Pacific Shipworm

☐ *Limnoria lignorum* — Gribble

☐ *Cirolana harfordi* — Marine Pillbug

☐ *Idotea wosnesenskii* — Rockweed Isopod

☐ *Traskorchestia traskiana* — Sandhopper

☐ *Axiothella rubrocincta* — Bamboo Worm

☐ *Leptosynapta clarki* — Burrowing Sea Cucumber

☐ *Polinices lewisii* — Lewis' Moon Snail

☐ *Dendraster excentricus* — Eccentric Sand Dollar

☐ *Nereocystis leutkeana* — Bull Kelp

☐ *Zostera marina* — Eelgrass

☐ *Epiactis prolifera* — Brooding Sea Anemone

☐ *Caprella laeviuscula* — Skeleton Shrimp

SEASHORE EXPLORING LOG

Location: _____

_____

Date: _____

Shore Type: _____

Tide Level:
☐ High
☐ Mid
☐ Low

Plant and Animal Species

(observe the size and colour, where found in intertidal region, and what other animals/plants are close by)

Vancouver Island Shores I

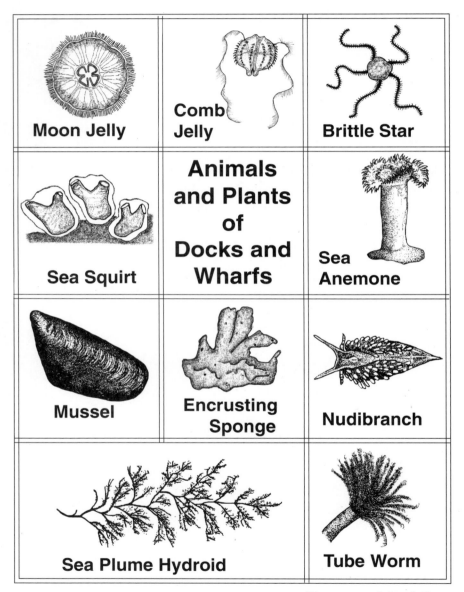

Moon Jelly

Comb Jelly

Brittle Star

Sea Squirt

Animals and Plants of Docks and Wharfs

Sea Anemone

Mussel

Encrusting Sponge

Nudibranch

Sea Plume Hydroid

Tube Worm

Vancouver Island Shores I

FLOATING DOCKS AND WHARF PILINGS

For a close-up look at many marine animals and plants that normally live below the low tide mark, the seashore explorer should venture onto a floating dock or wharf. Visibility is usually excellent since most wharves and docks are built in highly protected areas where waves are minimal.

Pilings provide view of intertidal zonation

Wharf pilings are permanently affixed to the sea bottom. They do not move up and down with the tides. During very low tides, the portion of the piling that is usually submerged under sea water is exposed to the open air.

Like the stripes on a barber's pole, the piling displays bands of attached shoreline animals. At the very top of the piling are the inhabitants of the high intertidal zone, such as the barnacle and mussel. The low intertidal zone to subtidal inhabitants are attached to the very bottom of the piling.

Animals and plants attached to floating docks

A huge number and variety of intertidal plants and animals cling to the edge of floating docks. Since the docks move up and down with the tides, the attached marine animals and plants are always submerged below the water surface and escape the daily exposure to air and sun.

During very low tide, it is sometimes possible to see from the floating dock, marine animals that normally live only in subtidal regions, such as the Sunflower Star, *Pycnopodia helianthoides*.

No matter what level of the tide, there are numerous floating animals like the jellyfish and comb jelly that pass by the dock and wharf.

On Floating Docks, Look For

1
Moon Jelly
2
Comb Jelly
3
Mussel and Mussel Worm
4
Brittle Star
5
Encrusting Sponge
6
Nudibranch
7
Hydroid
8
Sea Squirt
9
Sea Cauliflower
10
Sargassum Seaweed

Species and natural history of these creatures and plants are described in this chapter.

Tips for exploring along floating docks

✪ Investigate the shaded areas along the dock's edge which are typically covered with more varieties of plants and animals than sunny exposed sides.

✪ Lay down flat on the dock to get a closer view. Bring a cushion or pillow to soften the hard wood surface.

✪ All children and adult nonswimmers should wear life jackets.

Bioluminescence

On particularly dark nights, when the intertidal waters are still, swirl the surface waters with your arm or a paddle. Look carefully and you may see a low-level greenish-white light being emitted from the water. This light is produced by microscopic plankton.

Bioluminescent light can appear as a flash or in a steady glow. It is produced by a wide variety of both land and marine animals and plants. According to scientists, bioluminescence is not a particularly unique phenomenon. In the waters between 200 and 1,000 metres (61 to 3250 feet) of the open ocean, up to 80 per cent of the marine inhabitants emit light.

Sometimes incorrectly called phosphorescence (because the light emitted is very similar in colour to that emitted when phosphorus and oxygen mix), bioluminescence is created when the molecule lucifern and an enzyme called luciferase mix with oxygen. The molecule that is produced emits a light-producing photon but no form of heat is generated.

Scientists are a bit perplexed in explaining why so many animals have evolved with the ability to produce light. Some organisms may use it as a defensive weapon or to momentarily blind a predator, while others use it as an attractant during mating rituals.

Bioluminescent Marine Worm

The Moon Jelly

Everyone knows a jellyfish is not a fish. As a member of the Phylum Cnidaria [nee-dare-EE-ah], the jellyfish is related to the sea anemone and hydroid.

The Moon Jelly, *Aurelia aurita*, looks like a transparent upside-down bowl or umbrella. Its body or bell is composed of two layers, an internal sheath, which is the stomach or manubrium lining, and the outside sheath. Between the two is a gelatinous layer called the mesoglea which is composed of 96 per cent water.

In order to remain close to the water's surface, the jellyfish opens and closes its bell in a pulsating action. Like other plankton, it floats with the currents and tides. Around the edge of the rim of its bell are light-sensitive and balance organs.

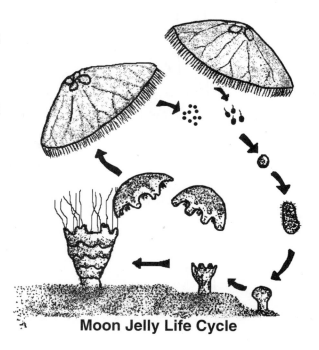

Moon Jelly Life Cycle

A carnivore

As carnivores, most jellyfish capture zooplankton on nemato-cyst-covered tentacles, which hang down from the edge of their umbrella. Prey is not caught at random. The jellyfish prefers certain plankton and has adapted specialized hunting behaviours to catch it. The Moon Jelly captures zooplankton in the mucous that coats the surface of its bell and oral arms. The prey is transferred to its mouth where it is absorbed inside the stalk or manubrium. Waste materials are expelled back up through the jellyfish's mouth.

Coloured gonads indicate gender

The horseshoe-shaped organs visible inside the Moon Jelly are its gonads or reproductive organs. Bluish-purple coloured gonads indicate a male, while whitish-yellow gonads indicate a female.

159

Life cycle takes on various physical forms

The Moon Jelly takes on very different physical forms through the various stages of its life cycle.

As a broadcast fertilizer, male and female jellyfish disperse sperm and eggs into the surrounding sea water. Fertilized eggs develop into free-drifting larvae. The larvae attach to a substrate and develop into a sessile polyp. The polyp looks like a stack of upside-down bowls or saucers. The "bowls" are attached to each other by a stem through each centre. Eventually the individual "bowls" or small Moon Jellies break free and drift away.

During the fall, it is not uncommon to see swarms of Moon Jellies all around the docks. These congregations increase the likelihood of successful reproduction.

Aurelia aurita

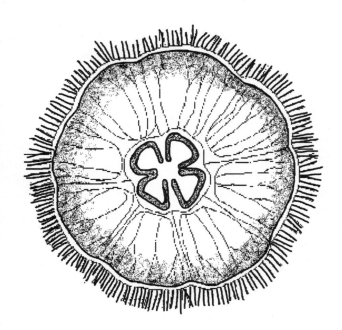

[Oar-EEL-ee-ah oar-EE-tah]
Common name: Moon Jelly
Where: near surface waters, occasionally washed up after storms or caught in high tides
Colour: whitish/blue transparent except for horseshoe-shaped reproductive organs which are variably coloured bluish-purple (indicates a male) or whitish/yellow (indicates a female)
Shape: saucer-shaped, short fringe-like tentacles
Size: up to 40 cm (16 inches) wide but typically 10 to 15 cm (4 to 6 inches) in coastal waters and 5 cm (2 inches) thick
Note: Not harmful to touch. Seen swarming around docks in the autumn or cast ashore after a storm.

Nematocysts and Colloblasts

Jellyfish, sea anemones and ctenophores have a very sophisticated method of catching their food. Waving tentacles are covered with specialized prey-capture cells that act like spring-loaded harpoons.

Nematocyst is a Latin word meaning thread bags. These minute organelles are housed within specialized cells called cnidocytes, located at the surface of the tentacles. A hollow filament explodes through the cell surfaces when touched or chemically stimulated.

There are over thirty known types of nematocysts. Some are barbed, like a fish hook, and inject a deadly toxin, while others are sticky and snare or entangle the prey. Most species of local jellyfish and sea anemones have nematocysts that will not harm humans.

Nematocysts discharge only once, and new ones are regenerated to replace the used artillery.

Colloblasts are found on the tentacles of ctenophores like the Sea Gooseberry, *Pleurobrachia bachei*. Each colloblast has a bulbous sticky surface head connected to a long straight filament and a spiral filament. When stimulated by a passing animal, the coiled filament snaps loose and catches the animal with a sticky mucous-like substance that is secreted from the end of the filament. The spiral filament is then contracted, and the animal is reeled in and transferred to the ctenophore's mouth.

Did you know that... some species of nudibranchs that prey on sea anemones eat undischarged nematocysts and use them for their own defense?

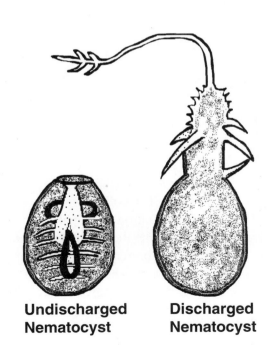

Undischarged Nematocyst   **Discharged Nematocyst**

161

The Comb Jelly

From its appearance, you may think that this transparent animal is related to the jellyfish, but it is not. The comb jelly is a member of the Phylum Ctenophora [teen-oh-FOUR-ah.] During the spring and summer months, the ctenophore or comb jelly is visible from the dock's edge.

No living relatives

Ctenophores have no known living relatives. There are only about 100 species of these amazing creatures on our planet, and they are the largest creatures to move by ciliary action.

Iridescent combs diffract sunight

Eight rows of ctenes [teens] run up and down the comb jelly's body. The ctenes or tiny hairs move or flap in a falling domino effect and propel the ctenophore through the water. The ctenes are iridescent, and on a sunny day, look carefully to see a kaleidoscope of colours diffracted through the combs.

At night, the comb jelly is bioluminescent and can be seen outlined in flashes of light. Although it is not understood why ctenophores bioluminescence, it is believed that this light may be produced to obscure its silhouette against the surface waters from predators in deeper waters.

Plankton eater

The comb jelly is a carnivorous predator that consumes sub-stantial amounts of microscopic zooplankton. Some species, such as the Sea Gooseberry, *Pleurobrachia bachei*, catch prey with two long sticky tentacles that are extended out from the sides of its body. The colloblast-covered tentacles are reeled in when enough zooplankton is caught.

Like the jellyfish, the ctenophore is a selective feeder. It places preferred plankton into its mouth which opens directly into the gullet. The gullet runs almost the length of the comb jelly's body. Inside there are two tubes which eventually turn into a single canal and an opening to the outside where waste material is shed.

Broadcast fertilizer

The comb jelly is a hermaphrodite that sheds sperm and eggs into the sea water. The fertilized eggs develop directly into creatures which, in many species, look like smaller replicas of their adult form.

A ctenophore's senses

Sensory receptors are located at the opposite side of the mouth. A light-sensitive organ at the centre tells the ctenophore when the light is dimming and when to propel itself toward the surface waters.

Pleurobrachia bachei

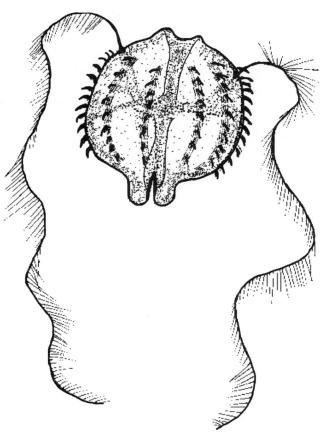

[Plurr-oh-BRAKE-ee-ah baa-KEY]
Common name: Sea Gooseberry, Cat's Eyes
Where: seen from floating docks, usually in large swarms
Shape: spherical balls with two long tentacles
Colour: transparent with iridescent combs
Size: up to 2 cm (.8 inches) wide
Note: As a carnivore, is known to eat herring and cod larvae in great quantities. Occasionally, these marble-sized ctenophores are stranded on the beach.

The Mussel

Considered the most common bivalve around the world, mussels establish themselves quickly along our shorelines by crowding together in dense clusters in the middle intertidal zone.

Massive clusters of shells

When standing on a dock, you'll notice that mussels are attached everywhere, clasping to dock lines in large round bundles, on styrofoam floats, on pilings and under the bows of many boats. Mussels are extremely abundant on rocky shorelines and are often so dense that mussel beds have been known to reach up to 40 centimetres (16 inches) thick. Inside these massive cluster of shells are trapped pockets of mud and silt, a perfect habitat for many other marine animals.

Secretes byssus threads to hang on

A mussel hangs on to a hard surface by byssus threads, exceedingly strong fibres that are secreted from a gland located in the mussel's small foot. The tip of the foot presses against a substrate, attaches the sticky end of the fibre and then withdraws the foot. The fibre hardens immediately in the sea water.

In order to maintain a secure position, the mussel produces numerous byssus threads, not unlike the ropes on a tent. The threads bear the strain of wave action and strong tidal currents, keeping the mussel securely attached.

With such a complex web of threads to maintain its position, it is hard to imagine that a mussel can move. However, if the mussel finds itself buried by sediment, it can cast off the fibres and produce new longer threads to pull itself along.

The mussel's shells are thin and wedge-shaped, always longer than higher.

Did you know that...

the larger California Mussel, *Mytilus californianus* is not found along the east coast of Vancouver Island? This thick-shelled mussel prefers the open waters of the unprotected West Coast.

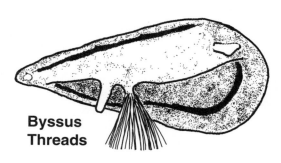

Byssus Threads

Plankton filter feeder

The siphons are extremely short and do not extend past the shell opening. The mussel keeps its shell slightly agape, and beating cilia create a current that draws sea water and accompanying plankton into its incurrent siphon.

Mussels filter large quantities of sea water per day and are used by scientists and aquaculturists to monitor pollution and PSP toxin levels in the Strait.

Broadcast fertilizers

Sexes are usually separate but hermaphrodite mussels have been found. Sperm and eggs are broadcast into the sea water in early spring.

For the natural history of bivalves, please refer to the chapter on "Mud Flats."

Mytilus trossulus

[My-TILL-us TROSS-uh-luss]
Common name: Blue Mussel, Edible Mussel
Where: attached to rocks, docks and any solid object
Zone: high to low intertidal
Colour: variable from blue black to yellow brown
Size: 7 to 9 cm (2.8 to 3.5 inches) long by 4 to 5 cm (1.6 to 2 inches) high
Shape: oblong oval, anterior pointed, posterior rounded
Shell: thin, with shiny periostracum and very fine concentric lines

Notes: Usually in dense masses; will tolerate brackish water. Recent scientific evaluation of the common blue mussel found so abundantly along the coastline has determined that it is a unique species, biochemically different from the Atlantic species *Mytilus edulis.*

The Mussel Worm

In amongst clusters of mussels, the seashore explorer is bound to find the voracious segmented worm called the Mussel Worm. Known for its ability to bite with two black extendible mandibles, caution should be used when handling this creature.

In the summer months, these worms swim from rock shelters and mussel beds into the open water to spawn. Through broadcast fertilization, they release gametes and die after spawning. For a natural history of marine worms, please refer to the chapter on "Mud Flats."

Nereis vexillosa

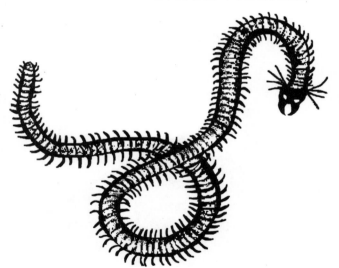

(=Nereis virens)

[NER-ice vex-il-OH-sah]

Common names: Mussel Worm, Clam Worm, Sand Worm

Where: mainly mud flats in shallow burrows, but can be found among barnacles and mussel beds or under rocks on gravel/cobblestone shores

Zone: high intertidal to subtidal

Shape: large and fleshy, thick head and body tapered to rear

Size: to 30 cm (12 inches) long

Colour: tan to blue/green, some are iridescent

Notes: Be very careful about picking up this worm! It possesses two black extendible biting mandibles that are used to tear up prey. These mandibles can "bite" human flesh. Eats algae, bivalves and other worms. Very active, swims and burrows rapidly with its parapodia. At night, they are attracted to lights around docks.

The Brittle Star

Brittle and fragile is an accurate description of the five-armed relative of the sea star, commonly called the brittle star. Because the calcareous plates in its flexible arms contain very little tissue, they tend to break off easily in a process referred to as autotomization.

The brittle star's wiry, slender arms emanate from a central disk, and the distinction between the disk and arms is clearly visible.

Although the arms do possess tube feet, they are used for eating rather than movement. As a detritus and small animal feeder, the tube feet are used to capture food and pass it toward the brittle star's mouth.

To move about, the brittle star swings its flexible arms about, using them to push and pull itself along. Because of the snakelike writhing of the arms, the brittle star was once referred to as the serpent star.

Most brittle stars reproduce through broadcast fertilization. A few species brood their eggs in special sacs or pockets under their arms.

Amphipholis squamata

(=*Axiognathus squamatus*)
[Am-fee-FOE-liss squaw-MAT-ah]
Common name: Small Brittle Star
Where: on sand and gravel, along docks and beneath rocks and in tidepools
Zone: high intertidal to subtidal
Size: about 3 cm (1.2 inches); arms about 4 times the diameter of the disk
Colour: gray with white bands or spots
Notes: Exceedingly fragile, do not pick up. Holds its eggs in little pockets that open to the outside near the bases of the arms.

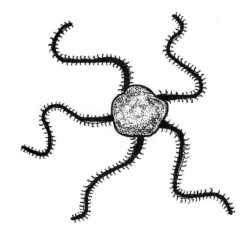

167

The Calcareous Tube Worm

Along the dock's edge, the seashore explorer is sure to notice small, almost flat, spiral-shaped shells attached to almost every hard surface. These are the homes of tube-dwelling sedentary annelid worms.

The calcareous or limy tube worm secretes a hard, protective shell around its body and remains inside its entire life.

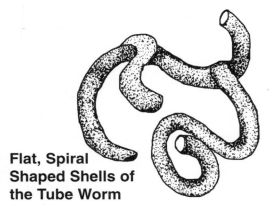

Flat, Spiral Shaped Shells of the Tube Worm

In order to feed and breathe, the worm extends a number of feathery tentacles near its mouth out into the sea water. Some tube worms collect plankton on sticky tentacles while others actually brush up deposits from the surrounding bottom surfaces.

When protruded, the crown of tentacles is often quite magnificent in colour and can be very ornate. Why these worms are so brightly coloured is not known. The plumes have long filaments with side branches and often resemble a feather. Cilia beat to create a current and draw water and accompanying plankton into the worm's mouth.

Operculum-like funnel closes off tube

Many tube worms have a funnel or trumpet-shaped centre-piece on the tentacles that is used much like a gastropod's operculum. When the tentacles are withdrawn, the trumpet closes off the opening of the calcareous tube to any potential predators.

Many tube worms have a light-sensitive organ which alerts them to any sudden change from dark to light. A passing shadow causes the worm to withdraw its tentacles, and all that remains visible to the seashore explorer standing on a dock is the calcareous tube. Should a predator eat the tentacles, the worm has excellent regenerative powers and can grow new ones. There is only one opening in the calcareous tube worm's shell, and all waste matter from the worm must be excreted out from this open end.

For more information about marine worms, please refer to the chapter on "Mud Flats."

Serpula vermicularis

[Sir-PEW-lah ver-mick-you-LAR-iss]
Common name: Calcareous Tube Worm
Where: on rocks, docks, shells
Zone: low intertidal to subtidal
Tube size and shape: up to 20 cm (8 inches) long and 2 cm (.8 inches) wide; coiled long hard white tube
Worm size: about 6 to 8 cm (2.4 to 3.15 inches) long
Plume shape and colour: fan-shaped with funnel or trumpet-shaped centre; red orange with whitish bands
Notes: Calcium carbonate is extracted from the sea water, and glands in a fold of the skin just behind the tentacles produce a ring of lime or hard shell.

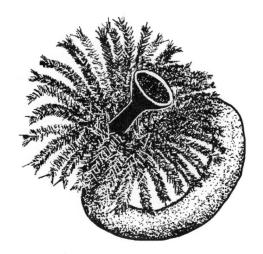

Eudistylia vancouveri

[You-dee-STY-lee-ah van-KOO-ver-eye]
Common names: Feather Duster Worm, Plume Worm, Parchment Tube Worm
Where: attached to boulders, and docks and pilings
Zone: low intertidal to subtidal
Tube size and shape: up to 1 cm (.4 inches) in diameter and up to 25 cm (10 inches) long
Plume shape and colour: featherlike fan shaped; reddish purple to brown, sometimes with green bands
Plume size: up to 6 cm (2.4 inches) across when fully expanded
Notes: Softer parchment-like tube, typically found in large numbers. Actual worm is only a fraction of the tube's length. Short, stiff bristles, which are modified parapodia, allow it to hold on to the side of its tube.

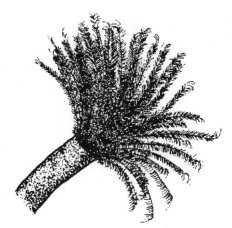

The Plumose Sea Anemone

It's difficult to imagine that one creature can vary its shape so radically, but the Plumose Sea Anemone can look like a flattened disk to a flower-like animal with an elongated stem.

Its highly frilled tentacles are loaded with nematocysts that assist in the capture of plankton. The tentacles located at the end of the stalk, wave about in the sea water.

The Plumose Sea Anemone can reproduce either sexually or asexually. One form of asexual reproduction is known as pedal laceration, a process involving the detachment of pieces of the pedal disk. Each piece develops into a new anemone.

For more information about sea anemones, see chapter on "Gravel and Cobblestone Beaches."

Metridium senile

[Me-try-DEE-um SEN-nil-ee]
Common names: Plumose Anemone, Frilled Anemone
Where: attached to rocks, docks, and any solid objects, including kelp fronds
Zone: low intertidal to subtidal
Colour: variable, reddish/brown to creamy/white
Size: 5 cm (2 inches) to 10 cm (4 inches) high
Notes: Highly variable size and shape from elongated stalk to almost flat disk. Frilled tentacles designed for feeding on plankton. Eaten by Shaggy Mouse Nudibranch, *Aeolida papillosa,* and the Leather Star, *Dermasterias imbricata.*

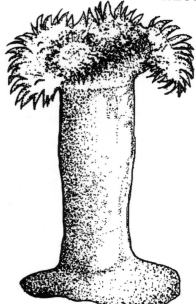

Plumose Anemone Fully Extended

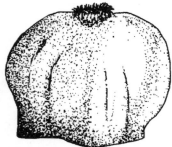

With Tentacles Withdrawn

Almost Flattened Disk

The Sunflower Star

The largest sea star in the world can often be seen on the sea bottom from floating docks and on many shorelines in the low intertidal zone at the very lowest tides.

A notorious predator, the Sunflower Star is noted for its speedy attack. It will consume most kinds of intertidal life such as sea urchins, worms, chitons, and other sea stars.

The Sunflower Star is able to move very quickly along the sea floor due to its soft calcareous non-jointed body and the tube feet on its 20 to 24 arms. This sea star is renowned for its ability to drop its arms at will to escape predators.

For more information about sea stars, please refer to the chapter on "Rocky Shores and Tidepools."

Pycnopodia helianthoides

[Pike-no-POD-ee-ah hell-ee-an-THOI-dees]
Common name: Sunflower Star
Where: on substrate seen from floating docks, rocky shores and soft sand/mud bottoms
Zone: low intertidal to subtidal
Colour: pinkish red to purple brown
Shape: very broad disk with 20 to 24 arms
Texture: soft and flexible, sticky mucous coated
Size: up to 80 cm (31 inches) from tip to tip
Notes: Born with only five or six arms. When many marine animals detect its scent, they make a hasty retreat.

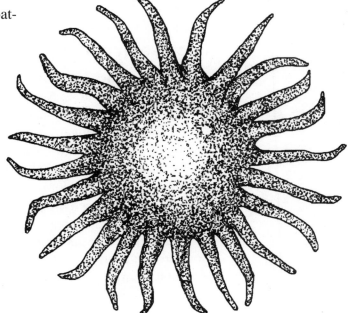

171

The Encrusting Sponge

Along the docks, look for thin irregular sheets of brightly coloured encrusting sponges. Touch one and you'll feel that it is soft and squishy.

Did you know that...
sponges are very simple multi-celled animals that take on a variety of shapes? Some are cup or vase shaped, while others are broadly branched or encrusting.

Basic multi-celled animal

The encrusting sponge is a very basic multi-celled animal and a member of the phylum Porifera. It has no tissues, internal organs, muscles, or digestive tract. It has a skeleton of sorts and, depending upon the species, is made of microscopic hard splinters called spicules or a tough protein called spongin.

Internal canals

Water enters the sponge's internal canals through small pores called ostia, and pass by specialized cells with flagella. Flagella are hairlike structures that create a constant, unidirectional water flow through the sponge's internal canals. Oxygen is absorbed at the cellular level while other specialized cells consume plankton. Water exits the sponge's internal cavities through the large visible openings called oscula.

Food source for intertidal animals

Many species of encrusting sponges produce toxins which may ward off predators. Nevertheless, they are eaten by certain snails, sea stars and some nudibranch species.

Encrusting sponges are able to reproduce either sexually or asexually. Most encrusting sponges have separate sexes. Sperm is broadcast in the water and absorbed inside the female body where fertilization occurs. Colonization of new substrates occurs by production of a dispersing planktonic larvae stage.

The encrusting sponge can live from several months to over 50 years depending upon the species. When environmental conditions are not conducive to the encrusting sponge, it is able to disintegrate temporarily and regenerate when conditions improve.

Halichondria bowerbanki

[Hal-ee-KON-dree-ah
bow-er-BANK-ee]]

Common name: Crumb of Bread Sponge
Where: on rocks, along docks and other solid objects
Zone: middle to low intertidal
Colour: orangish/yellow to green
Shape: encrusting sheets
Size: usually larger than 25 cm (10 inches) wide and 25 mm
(1 inch) thick or high
Texture: looks like bread crumbs
Notes: Often small torn-off pieces are found floating along docks. The Sea Lemon nudibranch, *Archidoris montereyensis*, is a common predator of this species.

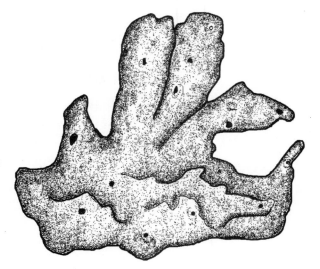

Ophlitaspongia pennata

[Off-lee-tah-SPONG-ee-ah pen-AT-ah]

Common name: Velvety Red Sponge
Where: rocks and docks, in crevices
Zone: middle to subtidal around
3 metres (10 feet) deep
Shape: encrusting sheets
Colour: red
Size: large up to almost a metre
(39 inches) wide but flat, up to
6 mm (.25 inches) thick
Texture: velvety soft with starlike pores that are close together.

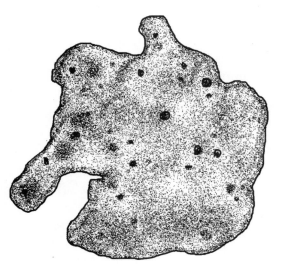

173

The Nudibranch

On pieces of drifting eelgrass and seaweed floating around docks, particularly in the late spring and early summer, look for tiny brightly coloured sea slugs called nudibranchs.

Gastropod without a shell

Unlike other gastropods, the nudibranch, which means "naked gills" in Latin, is unable to take refuge in a shell when predators approach. Many species of the nudibranch have developed bright colours and an unpleasant toxin to warn potential predators to stay away.

Dorid and aeolid nudibranchs

Two kinds of nudibranchs found locally are classified according to the location and appearance of their gills. The dorid nudibranch's body is flattened and plump and has its plume-like gills surrounding its anus. The aeolid nudibranch has finger or feather-like extensions of its digestive system, which act as gills, called cerata that cover the length of its back.

As a carnivore, the nudibranch eats hydroids, sea anemones, sponges and other nudibranchs, with a highly modified radula.

Amazingly, some species of nudibranchs that prey on cnidarians, like the sea anemone and hydroid, consume cnidocytes which contain stinging cells called nematocysts (see description in this chapter). The undischarged nematocysts are transferred and retained in the cerata on the nudibranch's back. When a predator approaches, the "borrowed" stinging cells are discharged.

The nudibranch is a hermaphrodite that copulates. Each nudibranch lays thousands of eggs in clusters or spiral bands. Free-swimming larvae eventually settle onto a substrate and mature into adults. Most live in subtidal regions.

Nudibranch Facts
Phylum: Mollusca, Class Gastropoda
Reproduction: hermaphrodites that copulate, eggs laid in mucous strings
Food: carnivores, eat with radula
Predators: few
Notes: Can be elusive but some are so beautiful, they are well worth looking for

---

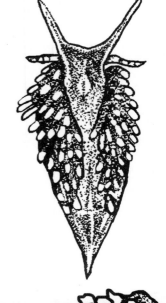

Hermissenda crassicornis

(=Phidiana crassicornis)

[Herm-ee-SEND-ah crass-ee-CORN-iss]

Common name: Opalescent Nudibranch

Where: on rocks, mudflats, on eelgrass floating about docks

Zone: low intertidal to subtidal

Shape: slender body, broadest just behind head which has two pairs of antennae; body is pointed at rear end

Colour: translucent white body with orange line down middle of back covered with orange cerata with opaque white tips

Size: up to 5 cm (2 inches) long and 1 cm (.4 inches) wide

Notes: Feeds on hydroids, sea squirts and different kinds of eggs.

Archidoris montereyensis

[Ark-ee-DOOR-iss mon-ter-ray-EN-sis]

Common name: Sea Lemon

Where: rocky shores, along docks

Zone: low intertidal to subtidal

Shape: elongated plump oval with two anterior hornlike rhinophores and posterior plume of pale yellow gills

Colour: dull orangish-yellow with black spots

Size: up to 12 cm (4.7 inches) long and 7 cm (2.8 inches) wide

Notes: Feeds on sponges and dead organic matter. A number of Pacific Northwest nudibranch species are called the Sea Lemon.

Aeolidea papillosa

[Ee-oh-LID-ee-ah pap-ee-LOW-sah]

Common name: Shaggy Mouse Nudibranch

Where: on rocks, cobblestone beaches, mudflats and on docks

Zone: from low intertidal to subtidal

Shape: thick body with two pairs of antennae and many cerata

Colour: variable but usually greyish brown

Size: up to 5 cm (2 inches) and 3 cm (1.2 inches) wide

Notes: Eats sea anemones; look near Plumose Anemone, *Metridium senile* on docks. Many slender cerata on back resemble fur, hence the common name "Shaggy Mouse."

The Sea Plume Hydroid

Don't be fooled by what appears to be a beige-brown fernlike plant swaying from the dock or piling. They are really animals, colonies of microscopic individual animals called hydroids.

Related to sea anemones and jellyfish

Hydroids are Cnidarians [nigh-dare-EE-anns], related to sea anemones and jellyfish. The Sea Plume Hydroid's stem and branches are fleshy tubes that connect all of the individual animals or polyps in the colony together. This hollow tube also acts as a common digestive tract.

Some polyps in the colony have mouths surrounded by a ring of nematocyst-covered tentacles (a description of nematocysts appears earlier in this chapter) that gather plankton. Other polyps function as the reproductive structures of the hydroid.

Alternation of generation life cycle

The Sea Plume Hydroid reproduces by alternation of generation in which one generation of hydroid is free-drifting and the next generation is attached to a substrate like a floating dock.

When it is in the fixed stage, little thin saucer-like medusae rupture from the reproductive polyps and become free-drifting animals.

Broadcast fertilizers

At their sexual maturity, these drifting hydroids broadcast eggs and sperm. The fertilized eggs develop into a round cilia-covered planula larva. After some drifting about, the planulae attach to a substrate and a new sessile or fixed hydroid colony begins. The cycle between two very different forms of life continues.

In winter, bushy colonies tend to die back to the base attached to the substrate. New colonies may grow back from these bases in spring.

Obelia sp.

[Oh-BEAL-ee-ah]

Common names: Sea Plume or Bushy Wineglass Hydroid

Where: attached to rocks, docks, shells and any solid object

Zone: low tide line to subtidal

Shape: highly branched colony

Colour: brownish-beige

Size: up to 20 cm (8 inches) high and 10 cm (4 inches) wide

Notes: *Obelia dichotoma* or *Obelia longissima* are two local species which are difficult to distinguish. Amphipods, like the Skeleton Shrimp, *Caprella laeviuscula,* commonly cling to *Obelia spp.* colonies.

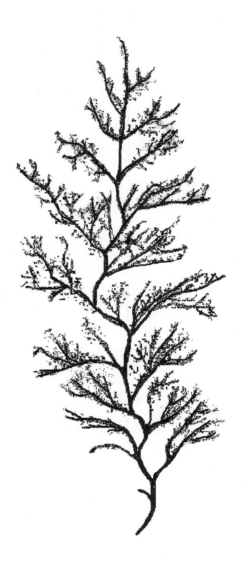

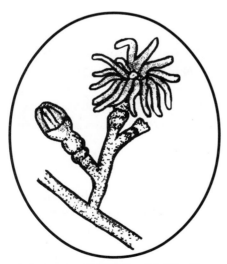

Microscopic View Of *Obelia sp.*

The Sea Squirt

The sea squirt is an intriguing marine creature. Although it is an invertebrate animal, biologists classify the sea squirt in the Phylum Chordata, along with all of the other vertebrate animals like fish and mammals. As a tadpole-like larvae, it has a notochord, a feature that is unique to the chordates. The notochord disappears in the sea squirt's adult form but this feature has long intrigued scientists from an evolutionary perspective.

Did you know that... the solitary sea squirt has a circulatory system with a heart that is able to change the direction in which it pumps blood through its body?

The sea squirt, a common name originating from the fact that it squirts water when disturbed, is also known as a "tunicate", referring to the covering or tunic that encloses the animal, or "ascidian", a Latin name meaning attached. The common name varies from field guide to field guide.

Sea squirts are divided into two groups: solitary sea squirts and compound or colonial sea squirts.

Solitary sea squirts

The solitary sea squirt is very variable in shape, body covering and colour. Some species are transparent, smooth and jelly-like; other species are colourful, wrinkled and leathery. As filter feeders, water is absorbed by the incurrent or mouth pore and passed through a tiny gill slit by ciliary action within the body walls. Plankton and detritus are trapped by mucous and drawn into the mouth. Waste matter and water are then discharged through the excurrent or atrial pore. Almost all species of solitary sea squirts are hermaphrodites that release eggs and sperm into the surrounding water.

Colonial or compound sea squirts

Often confused with encrusting sponges, the compound sea squirt can be distinguished by its hard gelatinous texture, shiny, slick surface and its uniformity in thickness. Attached to hard surfaces such as rocks or floating docks, some species of compound sea squirts contain individuals interconnected by stolons or runner-like structures. Other species form a mass of growth in which individuals live within one common sheath or tunic with one common siphons. Sea squirts extract plankton and detritus from the surrounding sea water through their incurrent siphon and expel used water through an excurrent siphon. Most species of compound sea squirts reproduce through asexual budding.

Aplidium californicum

[Ay-ply-DEE-um cal-ee-FOR-knee-come]
Common name: Sea Pork
Where: on rocks and docks and wharf pilings where there is some wave action
Zone: low intertidal
Colour: variable, brownish orange to pink
Shape: like an irregular pancake
Size: more than 20 cm (8 inches) in diameter and about 1 cm (.4 inches) thick
Notes: This compound sea squirt has a shiny jelly-like appearance.

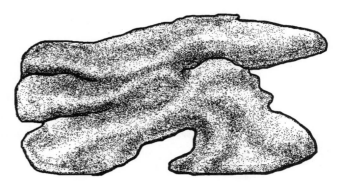

Corella willmeriana

[Core-ELL-ah will-mer-EE-ann-ah]
Common name: Transparent Sea Squirt
Where: on floating docks often attached to mussel beds or calcareous tube worms
Zone: low intertidal
Colour: transparent or frosted white
Shape: cylindrical lobe resembles elongated bubble on blister-pack used for packing or small ice cubes
Size: 3 cm (1.2 inches) high
Notes: Individuals may form a cluster which resembles a sheet of ice. Life span about one year.

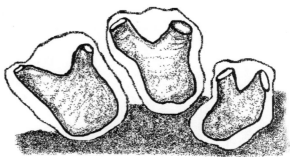

179

Seaweed:

Sargassum muticum

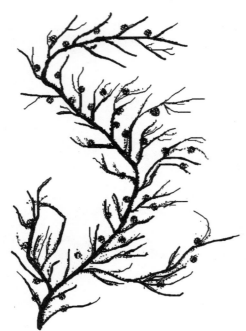

[Sar-GAS-um mew-TEA-cum]
Common name: Japanese Seaweed
Phylum: Phaetophyta or Brown Algae
Where: floats on water surface and spreads rapidly in slightly warm waters in bays and harbours
Colour: yellowish brown
Shape: many branched with fine small serrated edges.
Size: Small blades 1 to 2 cm (.4 to .8 inches) long
Notes: Small round floats that look like seeds are filled with gas to give the plant its buoyancy. Not a native seaweed but a Japanese species believed to have arrived with introduced oysters. Almost invasive in its ability to spread with the tidal currents.

Leathesia difformis

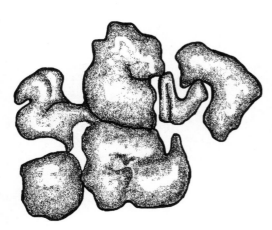

[Lee-THEES-ee-ah die-FORM-iss]
Common name: Sea Cauliflower
Phylum: Phaetophyta or Brown Algae
Where: attached to rocks and other algae
Colour: mustard-yellow green to olive green
Shape: small brain-shaped sack
Texture: appears sponge-like but has tough membrane
Size: about 4 to 5 cm (1.5 to 2 inches) in diameter
Notes: Usually found floating in amongst other algae around docks and on rocky shores.

Floating Docks and Wharf Pilings Species Checklist:

Aurelia aurita	Moon Jelly	☐
Pleurobrachia bachei	Sea Gooseberry	☐
Mytilus trossulus	Blue Mussel	☐
Nereis vexillosa	Mussel Worm	☐
Pycnopodia helianthoides	Sunflower Sea Star	☐
Serpula vermicularis	Calcareous Tube Worm	☐
Eudistylia vancouveri	Feather Duster Worm	☐
Metridium senile	Frilled Sea Anemone	☐
Amphipholis squamata	Small Brittle Star	☐
Halichondria bowerbanki	Crumb of Bread Sponge	☐
Ophlitaspongia pennata	Velvety Red Sponge	☐
Hermissenda crassicornis	Opalescent Nudibranch	☐
Archidoris montereyensis	Sea Lemon Nudibranch	☐
Aeolidea papillosa	Shaggy Mouse Nudibranch	☐
Obelia sp.	Sea Plume Hydroid	☐
Aplidium californicum	Sea Pork	☐
Corella willmeriana	Transparent Sea Squirt	☐
Sargassum muticum	Japanese Seaweed	☐
Leathesia difformis	Sea Cauliflower	☐

SEASHORE EXPLORING LOG

Location: _____

_____

Date: _____

Shore Type: _____

Tide Level:

☐ High

☐ Mid

☐ Low

Plant and Animal Species

(observe the size and colour, where found in intertidal region, and what other animals/plants are close by)

Vancouver Island Shores I

Selected Books
for Further Reading

Lewis' Moon Snail

Pacific Northwest field guides:

Beachcomber's Guide to Marine Life of the Pacific Northwest by Thomas M. Niesen. Gulf Publishing, 1997 (160 p.) ISBN: 0884151328
  Popular. Includes Vancouver, Washington, Oregon and Northern California.

Exploring the Seashore in British Columbia, Washington and Oregon by Gloria Snively. Gordon Soules Book Publishers, 1978 (240 p.) ISBN: 0919574254
  Popular. The classic quick reference guide to outer and inner coast species of invertebrates and shore birds.

National Audubon Society Field Guide to North American Seashore Creatures. Knopf, 1995 (813 p.) ISBN: 0394519930
  Popular. Although it includes the entire coast of North America, this guide has exceptional photographs and includes many of the species found locally.

National Audubon Society Pacific Coast by Bayard H. and Evelyn McConnaughey. Knopf, 1985 (633 p.) ISBN: 0394731301
  Popular. Superb photographs and general field guide to outer Pacific Coast.

Tidepool & Reef: Marinelife Guide to the Pacific Northwest Coast by Rick M. Harbo. Hancock House, 1980 (55 p.) ISBN: 0888390394
  Popular. Photographic guide to 130 species of marine invertebrates, fish and seaweed found on exposed and protected coastlines of British Columbia.

Seashore natural history and ecology:

Beachwalker: Sea Life of the West Coast by Stefani Hewlett Paine. Douglas & McIntyre, 1992 (170 p.) ISBN: 1550540165
Popular. Excellent introduction to the marine fauna of the Pacific Northwest, organized according to phylum.

Between Pacific Tides by E. Ricketts et al. Stanford University Press, 1985 (652p.) ISBN: 0804712298
Popular/Scholarly. The classic text that includes the natural history of many marine invertebrates and an introduction to intertidal zonation, ecology and biology. Extensive bibliography for each group of animals.

Pacific Seashores: A Guide to Intertidal Ecology by Thomas Carefoot. Vancouver, J.J. Douglas, 1977 (208 p.)
ISBN: 0888941218
Popular/Scholarly. Beautifully written introduction to Pacific Northwest seashore ecology by Professor Carefoot of University of British Columbia.

Seashore Life of the Northern Pacific Coast by Eugene N Kozloff. University of Washington Press, 1983 (370 p.)
ISBN: 0295960302
Scholarly/Popular. Extensive text documenting natural history and identification of marine invertebrates found on specific types of coastlines.

Mottled Star

Seashores by Herbert S. Zim and Lester Ingle. Golden Press, 1989 (160 p.) ISBN: 0307244962
Popular. Compact guide to animals and plants along shorelines in the United States. Part of the Golden Guide series.

Marine invertebrate animals:

British Columbia Museum Handbook Series

Scholarly/Popular. This scholarly series of handbooks provides information about the various species of marine animals and marine plants found in British Columbian waters. Although some handbooks are dated, the series is still very useful. Black and white photographs and illustrations.

Japanese Littleneck or Manila Clam

The Barnacles of British Columbia by Ira Cornwall. 1970 (69 p.) B.C. Museum Handbook no. 7

Intertidal bivalves of British Columbia by D.B. Quayle. 1960 (104 p.) B.C. Museum Handbook no. 17

Guide to Marine Life in British Columbia by George C. Carl. 1963 (135 p.) B.C. Museum Handbook no. 21

The Intertidal Univalves of British Columbia by Lela Griffith. 1967 (101p.) B.C. Museum Handbook no. 26

The Sea Stars of British Columbia by Philip Lambert, 1981 (153 p.) B.C. Museum Handbook no. 39.

Sea Cucumbers of British Columbia, Southeast Alaska, and Puget Sound by Philip Lambert. UBC Press, 1997 (166 p.) ISBN: 0774806079 BC Museum Handbook
  Scholarly/Popular. Written by the Curator of the Marine Invertebrate Department at the Royal British Columbia Museum.

Shells & Shellfish of the Pacific Northwest: A Field Guide by Rick M. Harbo. Harbour Publishing, 1997 (270 p.) ISBN: 1550171461
  Scholarly/Popular. Photographic guide to mollusks on inner and outer coasts of Oregon, Washington and British Columbia.

Algae/Seaweeds:

Common Seaweeds of the Pacific Coast by Robert J. Waaland. Pacific Search Press, 1977 (120 p.) ISBN: 09147181933

Guide to the Common Seaweeds of British Columbia by R.F. Scagel. (B.C. Museum Handbook no. 27) 1971.

Seaweeds at Ebb Tide by Muriel Guberlet. University of Washington Press, 1956 (182 p.) ISBN: 0295739282

Southeast Alaska's Rocky Shores: Seaweeds and Lichens by Rita M. O'Clair, Sandra C. Lindstrom, and Irwin R. Brodo. Plant Press, 1996 (152 p.)
  Scholarly/Popular. Many of the more common seaweeds found on east coast of Vancouver Island are included.

Seersucker

For young readers:

Oceans by Adrienne Mason. Kids Can Press, 1995 (80 p.) ISBN: 155074147
  A general introduction to the seas around the world. Discusses beaches, tides, sharks and many invertebrate and vertebrate marine animals.

Safari Beneath the Sea: the Wonder World of the North Pacific Coast by Diane Swanson. Whitecap Books, 1994 (58 p.) ISBN: 1551101467
  Superb colour photographs provided by Royal British Columbia Museum.

Squirts and Snails and Skinny Green Tails: Seashore Nature Activities for Kids by Diane Swanson. Whitecap Books, 1993 (64 p.) ISBN: 1551100622
  Includes 26 step-by-step activities for children at the beach.

Seashore by Steve Parker. Knopf, 1989 (63 p.) ISBN: 0394922549
  Beautifully illustrated and photographed introduction to the seashore and the animals that live there.

Travel Information Centres

Vancouver Island

Tourism Association of Vancouver Island
#302 - 45 Bastion Square
Victoria, BC V8W 1J1
(250) 382-3551

Discover Camping Reservation System
Reserve a camp site up to three months in advance at provincial and national parks in British Columbia. Credit cards accepted. 1-800-689-9025

BC Ferries
Information regarding schedules and fares to ferries to Vancouver and Gulf Islands.
1-888-223-3779
http://bcferries.bc.ca/ferries

BC Provincial Parks

BC Parks South Vancouver Island District
2930 Trans Canada Highway, RR #6
Victoria, BC V9B 5T9
(250) 391-2300
Interpretative program information: (250) 478-9414

BC Parks Strathcona District, Parksville Office
PO Box 1479
Parksville, BC V9P 2H4
(250) 954-4600

BC Parks Strathcona District, Black Creek Office
1812 Miracle Beach Drive
Black Creek, BC V9J 1K1
(250) 337-2400

Places Of Interest

Royal British Columbia Museum
675 Belleville Street
PO Box 9815,
Stn Prov Govt
Victoria, BC V8V 9W2
(250) 387-3701 or
1-800-661-5411
http://
rbcm1.rbcm.gov.bc.ca
Exhibits and information about the vertebrate and invertebrate inhabitants of the British Columbia intertidal region. Eco-tours to the seashore are available. Excellent book and gift shop. Admission charge.

Undersea Gardens
490 Belleville Street,
Victoria, BC V8V 1W9
(250) 382-5717
Located opposite the Parliament Buildings, visitors descend under water to view local marine life. Live diving show and touch tank. Gift shop. Admission charge.

Places Of Interest

Institute of Ocean Sciences

9860 West Saanich Road,
PO Box 6000
Sidney, BC V8L 4B2
(250) 363-6517
Free tours of the facilities
are given by appointment
only. Some hands-on exhibits discuss on-going ocea-
nography research.

The Marine Ecology Station

Cowichan Bay
Maritime Centre
1751 Cowichan Bay Road
RR#1, Cowichan Bay, BC
V0R 1N0
(250) 748-4522
http://mareco.org/
Floating laboratory offers
close-up views of marine
invertebrates through dis-
secting microscopes and in
aquaria. Summer courses
available. Gift shop.
Admission charge.

Victoria/Saanich Pennisula

Tourism Victoria
812 Wharf Street
Victoria, BC V8W 1T3
(250) 382-1131 or 1-800-663-3883

Capital Regional District (CRD) Parks
490 Atkins Avenue
Victoria, BC V9B 2Z8
(250) 474-7275 or (250) 478-3344
http://vvv.com/crd/parkhome.html

Saanich Peninsula Chamber of Commerce
PO Box 2014
Sidney, BC V8L 3S3
(250) 656-0525

Sidney Island Ferry
Departs seven days a week on the half hour
mid-May to September. (250) 727-7700

Gulf Islands

Saltspring Travel Infocentre
121 Fulford-Ganges Road, PO Box 111
Saltspring Island, BC V0S 1E0
(250) 537-5252

Galiano Island Visitor Association
General Delivery, Galiano Island, BC V0N 1P0
(250) 539-2233

Gabriola Chamber of Commerce Visitor Infocentre
575 North Road, Box 249
Gabriola Island, BC V0R 1X0
(250) 247-9332
http://www.island.net/~gabriola or gabriola@island.net

Cowichan/Duncan

South Cowichan Chamber of Commerce
Frayne Centre of Trans Canada Highway, RR#1,
Mill Bay, BC V0R 2P0
(250) 743-3566

Cowichan Valley Regional District Office
137 Evans Street
Duncan, BC V9L 1P5
(250) 746-2500

Duncan Chamber of Commerce
381 Trans Canada Highway
Duncan, BC V9L 3K5
(250) 746-4636

Crofton Infocentre
PO Box 128
Crofton, BC V0R 1Q0
(250) 246-2455 (seasonal)

Ladysmith/Nanaimo

Town of Ladysmith
410 Esplanade, Box 220
Ladysmith, BC V0R 2E0
(250) 245-6400

Tourism Nanaimo Infocentre
Beban House, 2290 Bowen Road
Nanaimo, BC V9T 3K7
(250)756-0106 or 1-800-663-7337
http:// tourism.nanaimo.bc.ca or
info@tourism.nanaimo.bc.ca

Newcastle Island Ferry
Foot passengers only. Departs from Maffeo
Sutton Park May to October. (250) 753-5141

Events Of Interest

Brant Wildlife Festival
PO Box 327,
Parksville, BC V9P 2G5
(250) 248-4117
http://www.island.net/~bfest
e-mail: bfest@island.net

A celebration of local wildlife and the return of the migrating Black Brant goose to offshore waters. Numerous venues include wildlife carving show, photograph exhibit, birding competition and Brant geese viewing areas along beach front.

Eelgrass: a favourite food source for the Black Brant goose

Parksville/Qualicum

Parksville-Qualicum Beach Tourism Association
(250) 752-2388

Parksville Travel Infocentre
Box 99
Parksville, BC V9P 2G3
(250) 248-3613

Qualicum Beach Travel Infocentre
2711 West Island Highway
Qualicum Beach, BC V9K 2C4
(250) 752-2923

Denman and Hornby Islands

Denman/Hornby Tourist Services
Denman Island, BC V0R 1T0
(250) 335-8313 or 2293

Comox/Courtenay

Comox Valley Travel Infocentre
2040 Cliffe Avenue
Courtenay, BC V9N 2L3
(250) 334-3234
http://www.tourism-comox-valley.bc.ca

Kin Beach Provincial Park
Grant and Ann Hamilton, Park Managers
1712 Astra Road
Comox, BC V9N 8B5
(250) 339-6365

Environmental Information

Georgia Strait Alliance
201- 195 Commercial Street,
Nanaimo, BC V9R 5G5
(250) 753-3459
http://www.island.net/~gsa

Non-profit organization provides information about the Strait of Georgia eco-system.

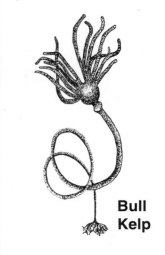

Bull Kelp

Index

Index

Scientific names are in *italics*.

Scientific names are in *italics*.

Index

Scientific names are in *italics*.

Index

Scientific names are in *italics*.

Index

Protected Shores of Vancouver Island

#266, 9B-1150
N. Terminal Avenue
Nanaimo, British Columbia
V9S 5T8 Canada

Telephone and Fax: 250-390-1887
or toll free in Canada and US
1-888-390-1887
e-mail: orders@proshores.com

www.proshores.com

To order more copies or enquire about other books and products available, please fax, phone, mail or e-mail us.

Check out our web site for:

- complete list of **field guides, books**, and **videos** on exploring nature in the Pacific Northwest

- links to **natural history sites** about Vancouver Island and British Columbia

- info about **scuba diving, kayaking, sailing** and **nature tours** on Vancouver Island

- links to Vancouver Island **travel and tourism** information centres

Please send ___ copy(ies) of
Vancouver Island Shores I (ISBN: 0-9682002-0-6)
at $18.95 (plus $4.00 shipping and handling) each to:

Name: _____

Mailing Address: _____

City & Province: _____

Postal Code: _____

Phone or e-mail address: _____

Cheques should be made out to: Protected Shores of Vancouver Island.
~~Residents of BC must include provincial and federal sales tax. ($25.88 total per copy.)~~
For U.S orders, please call or write for order information.